FAVORITES

Number Four

A Collection of Gospel Songs
for
SOLO, DUET, TRIO, QUARTET
and
GROUP SINGING

Compiled by
ALFRED B. SMITH

•

© 1956 by Singspiration, Inc. All rights reserved.

PRICE $1.00 EACH

Available at all Book and Music Stores

Singspiration® *Inc.*
WORLD DISTRIBUTORS
ZONDERVAN PUBLISHING HOUSE
GRAND RAPIDS, MICHIGAN 49506

A worthy addition indeed to the Singspiration series is FAVORITES No. 4. You will find it filled with gems of song. Each has been chosen for its merit in both word content and singability.

Some are rather new, others have had years of testing—but all are destined, I feel sure, to be favorites 'til we sing Redemption's story around the throne.

"Sing"cerely,
Alfred B. Smith

1   ONLY ONE LIFE

Avis B. Christiansen   Merrill Dunlop

1. On-ly one life to of-fer, Jesus my Lord and King;
2. On-ly this hour is mine, Lord; May it be used for Thee;
3. On-ly one life to of-fer, Take it, dear Lord, I pray;

On-ly one tongue to praise Thee, And of Thy mer-cy sing (for-ev-er);
May ev-'ry pass-ing mo-ment Count for e-ter-ni-ty (my Sav-ior);
Nothing from Thee with-hold-ing, Thy will I now o-bey (my Je-sus);

On-ly one heart's de-vo-tion,—Sav-ior, oh, may it be Con-se-
Souls all a-bout are dy-ing, Dy-ing in sin and shame; Help me
Thou who hast free-ly giv-en Thine all in all for me, Claim this

cra-ted a-lone to Thy match-less glo-ry, Yield-ed ful-ly to Thee.
bring them the message of Calv'ry's redemption In Thy glo-ri-ous name.
life for Thine own to be used, my Sav-ior, Ev-'ry mo-ment for Thee.

Copyright 1937. Renewal 1965 by Merrill Dunlop. Assigned to Singspiration, Inc. All rights reserved.

GOD DID A WONDERFUL THING FOR ME   2

J. W. P.
John W. Peterson

1. I was a sin-ner all cov-ered with shame, Lost and de-filed with no
2. Could I for-get it—that won-der-ful time When I was saved? 'twas a
3. Num-ber-less bless-ings He since has be-stowed, Mer-cies from Heav-en like

mer-it to claim, Some-how God loved me in spite of my sin—
mo-ment sub-lime! All thru life's jour-ney I'll sing of His love,
riv-ers have flowed; So man-y won-der-ful things He has done,

Chorus

Saved me, re-deemed me and cleansed me with-in.
Some-day I'll tell it to an-gels a-bove. God did a won-der-ful
And, praise His name, He has on-ly be-gun!

thing for me, One glo-ri-ous hap-py day, God did a won-der-ful

1-2 thing for me, When He took all my sin a-way. *3* took all my sin a-way.

© 1956 by Alfred B. Smith. Assigned to Singspiration, Inc. All rights reserved.

3. GOD HATH NOT PROMISED

Annie Johnson Flint
Alfred B. Smith

Duet

1. God hath not prom-ised skies al-ways blue, Flow-er-strewn path-ways
2. God hath not prom-ised we shall not know Toil and temp-ta-tions,
3. God hath not prom-ised smooth roads and wide, Swift, eas-y trav-el,

all our lives thro'; God hath not prom-ised sun with-out rain,
trou-ble and woe; He hath not told us we shall not bear
need-ing no guide; Nev-er a moun-tain, rock-y and steep,

CHORUS

Joy with-out sor-row, peace with-out pain.
Man-y a bur-den, man-y a care. But God hath prom-ised
Nev-er a riv-er tur-bid and deep. *Melody*

Melody in alto

strength for the day, Rest for the la-bor, light for the way, Grace for the

tri-als help from a-bove, Un-fail-ing kind-ness, un-dy-ing love.

Copyright 1952 by Alfred B. Smith. Assigned to Singspiration, Inc. All rights reserved.
Words permission Evangelical Publishers.

IN TIMES LIKE THESE

4

Mrs. R. C. J.
Mrs. Ruth Caye Jones

1. In times like these you need a Saviour, In times like these you need an anchor; [D.S.] Be very sure (Be very sure),
2. In times like these you need the Bible, In times like these, oh, be not idle; [D.S.] Be very sure (Be very sure),
3. In times like these I have a Saviour, In times like these, I have an anchor; [D.S.] I'm very sure (I'm very sure),

Be very sure (Be very sure), Your anchor holds and grips the Solid Rock!
Be very sure (Be very sure), Your anchor holds and grips the Solid Rock!
I'm very sure (I'm very sure), My anchor holds and grips the Solid Rock!

FINE REFRAIN

This Rock is Jesus, Yes, He's the One, This Rock is Jesus,—The only One;

D.S.

Copyright 1944 by Zondervan Music Publishers. All rights reserved. Used by permission.

5 WHEN GOD IS NEAR

A. H. A.
© COPYRIGHT 1939. RENEWED 1967 BY THE RODEHEAVER CO., OWNER.
INTERNATIONAL COPYRIGHT SECURED.
ALL RIGHTS RESERVED.
A. H. Ackley

SOLO

1. When God is near, with light my path is glow-ing, The cup of life with
2. When God is near the heav-y load is lift-ed, And ev-'ry du-ty
3. When God is near the tempt-er can-not lure me, The peace of God sur-

glad-ness o-ver-flows, ... And in the gar-den of my heart is
charms me with de-light; ... The clouds of sor-row by His love are
pass-ing sweet is mine; ... "Joint heir with Christ," His mercies re-as-

grow-ing The flow'r of love more fragrant than the sweetest rose. ....
rift-ed, And songs of joy my soul keeps singing in the night. ....
sure me, And some day I shall dwell with Him in realms di-vine ....

REFRAIN

When God is near, so near I hear Him speak to me, My ev-'ry

need His boundless grace sup-plies; When God is near my heart is filled with

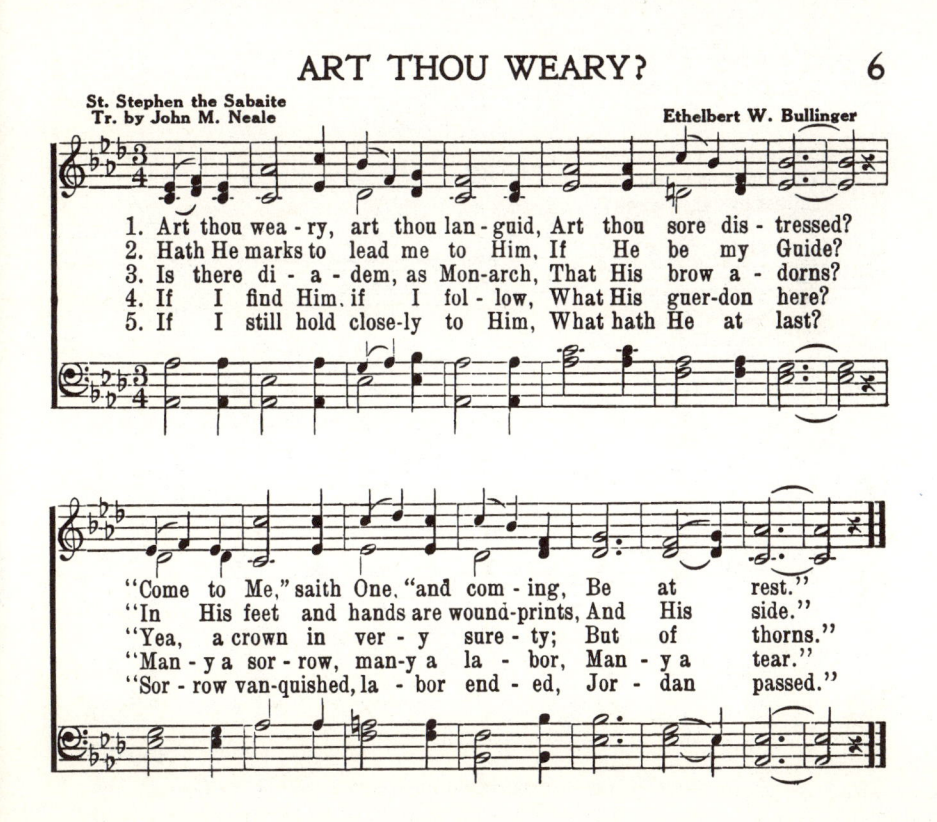

WHEN GOD IS NEAR

ec-sta-sy, And all the world's a par-a-dise when God is near, ...

And all the world's a par-a-dise when God is near. ...

ART THOU WEARY? 6

St. Stephen the Sabaite
Tr. by John M. Neale

Ethelbert W. Bullinger

1. Art thou wea-ry, art thou lan-guid, Art thou sore dis-tressed?
2. Hath He marks to lead me to Him, If He be my Guide?
3. Is there di-a-dem, as Mon-arch, That His brow a-dorns?
4. If I find Him, if I fol-low, What His guer-don here?
5. If I still hold close-ly to Him, What hath He at last?

"Come to Me," saith One, "and com-ing, Be at rest."
"In His feet and hands are wound-prints, And His side."
"Yea, a crown in ver-y sure-ty; But of thorns."
"Man-y a sor-row, man-y a la-bor, Man-y a tear."
"Sor-row van-quished, la-bor end-ed, Jor-dan passed."

7 THE RICHES OF LOVE

Rev. H. B. Hartzier
Duet

N. B. Sargent Arr.

1. The treasures of earth are not mine, I hold not its silver and gold: But a treasure far greater is mine; I have riches of value untold.
2. The treasures of earth must all fail, Its riches and honor decay, But the riches of love that are mine, E-ven death can not take them away.
3. Compared with the riches of love, The wealth of the world is but dross, I will seek but Christ Jesus to win, And for Him I count all things but loss.
4. Come, take of the riches of Christ, Exhaustless, and free is the store, Of its wonderful fulness receive, Till you hunger and thirst nevermore.

CHORUS

Oh, the depths of the riches of love, The riches of love in Christ Jesus, Far better than gold, or wealth untold, Are the riches of love in Christ Jesus.

© 1956 by Alfred B. Smith. Assigned to Singspiration, Inc. All rights reserved.

HE KEEPS ON LOVING US STILL

8

COPYRIGHT, 1931, RENEWAL, 1959
THE RODEHEAVER CO., OWNER
INTERNATIONAL COPYRIGHT SECURED

Herbert Buffum Haldor Lillenas

1. Though far you may wan-der a-way from the fold, Re-fus-ing to yield to His will, This thought is so pre-cious, al-though it be old:
2. His love is far great-er than mor-tals have known, His mer-cy the whole earth doth fill; To those who de-ny Him what pa-tience is shown!
3. Though fa-ther or moth-er for-sake us, we know This lov-er of souls nev-er will; He fol-lows our foot-steps, wher-e'er they may go,
4. Should we for-sake Him and our love be-come cold, No lon-ger our hearts feel the thrill That once we en-joyed when we en-tered His fold,

CHORUS

"He keeps on lov-ing us still."
He keeps on lov-ing us still.
And keeps on lov-ing us still.
He will keep on lov-ing us still.

He keeps on lov-ing us still, ... He keeps on lov-ing us still. . . . . Come lov-ing us still, lov-ing us still, loss or come gain, Thru sun-shine or rain, He keeps on lov-ing us still.

9 THERE IS NO GREATER LOVE

J. W. P.
John. W. Peterson

1. The love of friend and lov-er Is oft-en sweet-ly sung, But no
2. With val-ue more than mon-ey, Or jew-els rich and rare; There is
3. If He had died for an-gels Or ser-a-phim on high, We could

great-er love than the Sav-iour's love Can be told by mor-tal tongue.
naught on earth of an e-qual worth Oh, His love's be-yond com-pare!
un-der-stand, but a-mazed we stand That for sin-ners lost He'd die!

Chorus

There is no great-er love Than that of Christ a-bove, That made Him

stoop to earth, be-come a man, And by His death pro-vide re-demp-tion's plan;

There is no great-er love, That's why I'm sing-ing of God's love so

© 1955 by John W. Peterson. Assigned to Singspiration, Inc. All rights reserved.

THERE IS NO GREATER LOVE

rich and free, Re-vealed at Cal-va-ry — There is no great-er love.

JUST ONE GLIMPSE 10

N. B. V.
N. B. Vandall

1. When I was wand'ring on sin's downward road, Brok-en and help-less was I;
2. Je - sus spoke peace to my sin-burdened soul, Lo, at the sound of His voice
3. Now I'm re-joic-ing as on-ward I go, Sing-ing the sto-ry of grace;

I was lost and undone, crushed under the load, But some bod-y heard my cry.
I fell at His feet and my bur-den was gone, I made Him for-ev-er my choice.
To Him I'll be true what-ev - er the cost, And look once again on His face.

CHORUS

Just one glimpse, just one glimpse, That was e-nough for me; (for me;)

Just one glimpse, just one glimpse, That was e-nough for me.

Copyright 1954 by Singspiration, Inc. All rights reserved.

KNOWN ONLY TO HIM

Words and Music by
STUART HAMBLEN

Moderately

VERSE

1. When my eyes be-hold the stars this heart of mine is filled with won-der. My poor mind can-not grasp their ar-ray.
2. (In this) world of fear and doubt on my knees I ask the ques-tion, Why a lone-ly, heav-y cross I must bear.

But the hand that spilled them there all a-cross the wide
Then He tells me in my prayer it's be-cause I am trust-

Copyright 1952 by Hamblen Music Co.
Copyright assigned 1952 to **HILL AND RANGE SONGS, INC.**, New York, N. Y.
International Copyright Secured   Printed in U.S.A.
All rights reserved including the right of public performance for profit.

KNOWN ONLY TO HIM

heav - ens had a plan when He placed them that way.
worth - y He gives me strength, far more than my share.

CHORUS

Known On - ly To Him are the great hid-den se - crets. I'll fear not the dark-ness when my flame shall dim. I know not what the fu-ture holds, but I know who holds the fu-ture; it's a se-cret Known On - ly To Him. 2. In this Him.

12 LORD, I WANT A DIADEM!

SPIRITUAL

M. D.
Solo. *Brightly*

Merrill Dunlop

1. Lord, I want a shin-ing di - a-dem When I reach yon heav'n-ly land; What must I do, my Lord, to gain a di - a-dem When I reach that gold-en strand? "O you must run, run the race that's set be-fore you, You must run right straight and nev-er turn a-side To the
2. Lord, I want a shin-ing di - a-dem When I reach yon heav'n-ly land; What must I do, my Lord, to gain a di - a-dem When I reach that gold-en strand? "O you must fight, fight the world, the flesh, the dev-il, Nev-er fal-ter, nor grow wea-ry in the strife, For the
3. Lord, I want a shin-ing di - a-dem When I reach yon heav'n-ly land; What must I do, my Lord, to gain a di - a-dem When I reach that gold-en strand? "Take up your cross and be sure to bear it dai-ly And en-dure temp-ta-tion; nev-er yield to sin, For the
4. When I gain my shin-ing di - a-dem On the bless-ed heav'n-ly shore, I'm goin' to cast my di - a-dem at Je - sus' feet And a-dore Him ev-er-more. To Him be pow'r, hon-or, love and ad-o-ra-tion, Let my soul as-cribe all glo-ry to His Name; When the

Copyright 1941. Renewal 1969 by Merrill Dunlop. Assigned to Singspiration, Inc.
All rights reserved.

LORD, I WANT A DIADEM!

left, the right, and keep your eyes on Je-sus,—That's the way to win a
Lord hath trod the bit-ter way be-fore thee,—That's the way to win a
Lord will give you o-ver-com-ing vic-t'ry,—That's the way to win a
race is run, and ev-'ry bat-tle's o-ver,—At His feet I'll lay my

REFRAIN *(After 4th stanza)*

shining crown!" Oh, a shin-ing crown, Yes, my Lord, a star-ry

crown, I'm goin' to win my crown, So help me, Lord, And glo-ri-fy Thy Name.

PERFECT PEACE 13

Edward H. Bickersteth
In rather slow time

Alt. from George T. Caldbeck
by Charles J. Vincent

1. Peace, perfect peace, in this dark world of sin? The blood of Jesus whispers peace with-in.
2. Peace, perfect peace, with sorrows surging round? On Je-sus' bos-om naught but calm is found.
3. Peace, perfect peace, our future all unknown? Je-sus we know, and He is on the throne.
4. Peace, perfect peace, death shadowing us and ours? Je-sus has vanquished death and all its powers.
5. It is enough: earth's struggles soon shall cease, And Je-sus call us to heaven's per-fect peace.

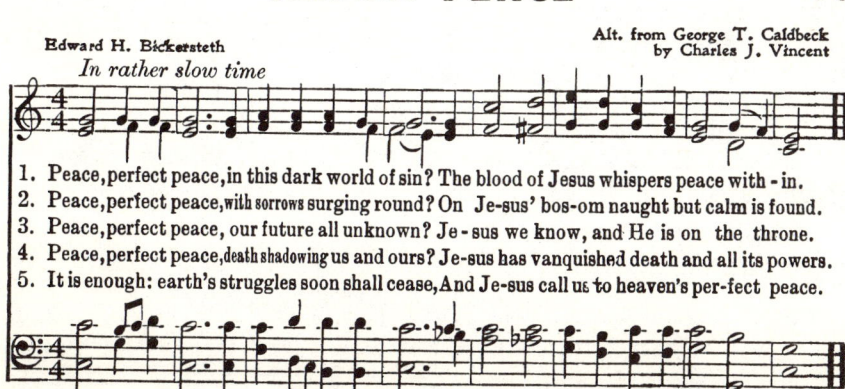

14 I LOVE TO THINK OF JESUS

COPYRIGHT 1919, RENEWAL 1947. THE RODEHEAVER CO., OWNER
INTERNATIONAL COPYRIGHT SECURED

C. Austin Miles
Adam Geibel

Solo or All in Unison

1. I love to think of Je-sus, who else could it be, Who could come down from
2. I love to think that He has giv-en me a part In par-don that He
3. I love to think of Je-sus when I am dis-trest, To think up-on His
4. I love to think of Him when tears of sor-row fall, To know that He has

heav'n to save a soul like me? To think of Him does not re-pay the
pur-chased with a bro-ken heart; And oft my eyes are fill'd with tears as
prom-ise brings a bliss-ful rest; In sor-row, pain and an-guish He is
suf-fered and He knows it all; It gives me strength to bear my bur-dens

debt I owe, I'll do my best my grat-i-tude to show
I re-call What He has done for me, and for us all
near I know, It is no won-der that I love Him so
nor com-plain, I nev-er yet have called to Him in vain,

Two-Part Chorus

I love to think of Je-sus, I
love to think of Je-sus and His love for me; My

love to think of Je-sus,
soul is lost in won-der that such love could be; I've known the love of mother, Of

I LOVE TO THINK OF JESUS

sis-ter, friend and brother, Like Jesus there's no other, He's more than all to me.

SINGING I GO

E. E. Hewitt
Wm. J. Kirkpatrick

1. The trust-ing heart to Je-sus clings, Nor an-y ill for-bodes,
2. The pass-ing days bring man-y cares, "Fear not," I hear Him say,
3. He tells me of my Fa-ther's love, And nev-er-slum-b'ring eye,
4. When to the throne of grace I flee, I find the prom-ise true,

But at the cross of Cal-v'ry, sings, Praise God for lift-ed loads!
And when my fears are turned to pray'rs, The bur-dens slip a-way.
My ev-er-last-ing King a-bove Will all my needs sup-ply.
The might-y arms up-hold-ing me Will bear my bur-dens too.

Chorus

Sing-ing I go a-long life's road, Prais-ing the Lord, prais-ing the Lord,

rit. ad lib.

Sing-ing I go a-long life's road, For Je-sus has lift-ed my load.

16 PEARLY GATES

S. E. C.
Alfred B. Smith and
Sidney E. Cox

1. There's a City with foundations just beyond the sunset glow,
2. Loved ones there await our coming—we have missed them for a while,
3. There will be one central Glory as we walk the golden street,

Pearly gates and walls of jasper, we are told; Where the
Then the gladness of their greeting we shall hear; We shall
Our dear Saviour, who redeemed us by His grace. He a-

ransom'd ones are wearing garments whiter than the snow, And the
know their happy voices, and the hand-shake and the smile, And we'll
lone will be the Glory as we gather at His feet, And our

Chorus

paving stones are made of purest gold. Pearly gates, pearly
join them in their singing loud and clear. Pearly gates,
eyes will only see His lovely face.

gates, In that City with the pearly gates; What a meeting, what a
pearly gates,

© 1956 by Alfred B. Smith. Assigned to Singspiration, Inc. All rights reserved.

PEARLY GATES

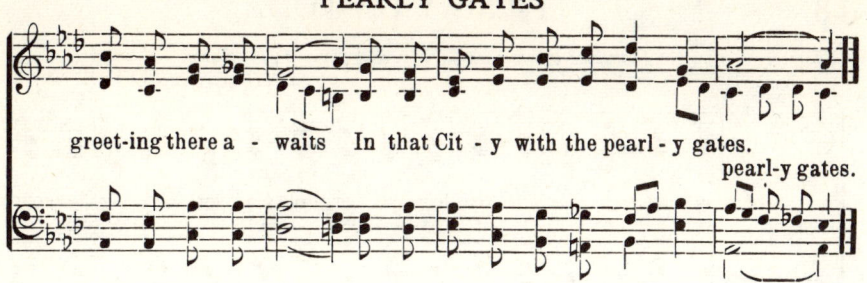

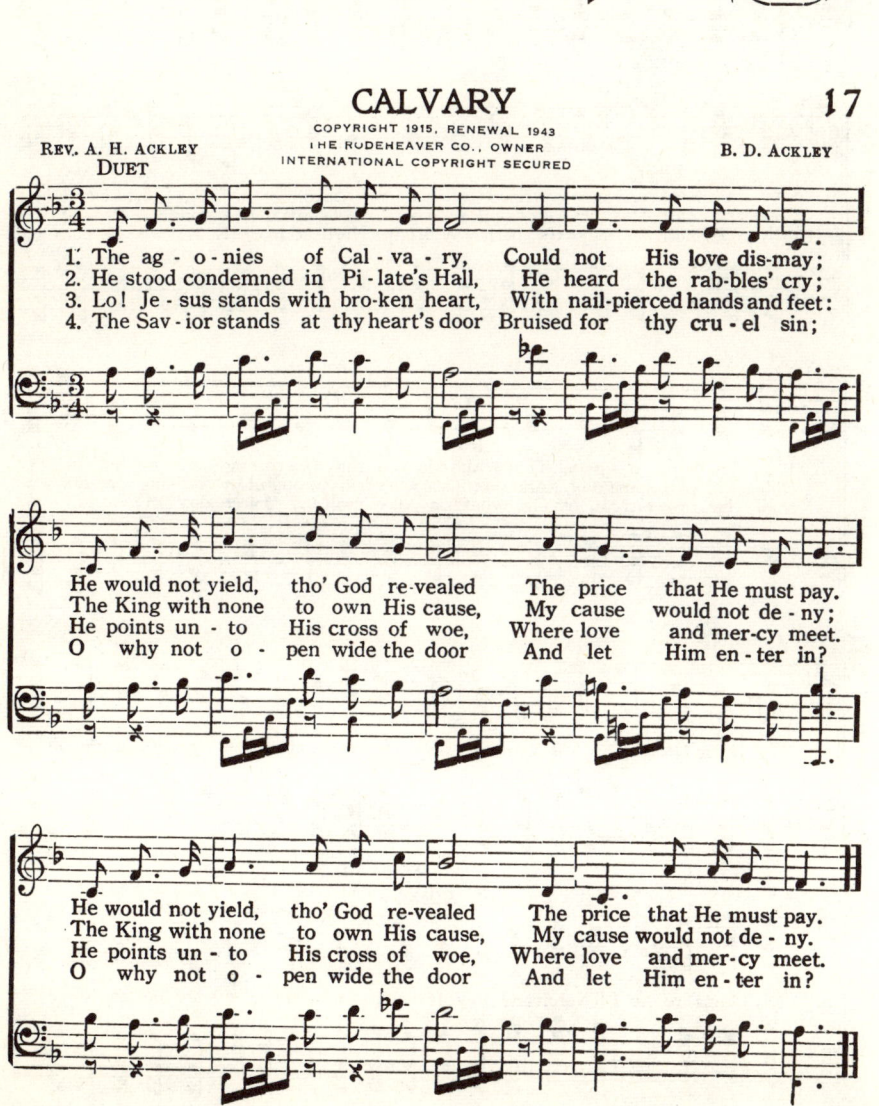

greet-ing there a - waits In that Cit - y with the pearl - y gates.
pearl-y gates.

CALVARY

17

COPYRIGHT 1915, RENEWAL 1943
THE RODEHEAVER CO., OWNER
INTERNATIONAL COPYRIGHT SECURED

REV. A. H. ACKLEY
DUET

B. D. ACKLEY

1. The ag - o - nies of Cal - va - ry, Could not His love dis-may;
2. He stood condemned in Pi - late's Hall, He heard the rab-bles' cry;
3. Lo! Je - sus stands with bro-ken heart, With nail-pierced hands and feet:
4. The Sav - ior stands at thy heart's door Bruised for thy cru - el sin;

He would not yield, tho' God re-vealed The price that He must pay.
The King with none to own His cause, My cause would not de - ny;
He points un - to His cross of woe, Where love and mer-cy meet.
O why not o - pen wide the door And let Him en - ter in?

He would not yield, tho' God re-vealed The price that He must pay.
The King with none to own His cause, My cause would not de - ny.
He points un - to His cross of woe, Where love and mer-cy meet.
O why not o - pen wide the door And let Him en - ter in?

18   IT MAY BE TODAY

Inscribed to my parents, Mr. and Mrs. W. H. Bush

B. B. B.   BEATRICE BUSH BIXLER

1. There is a message written In the Word of God for me; My Saviour put it there to ease my load of care. I read "Let not your heart be troubled I will come again, That with Me you may be, throughout eternity."
2. So many hearts are broken here, So many tears are shed, But Jesus gives sweet peace, This message brings relief. He'll come again for those He loves, The clouds will part some day, And Jesus will break through, I'm going up, are you?
3. This is the Christian's hope, And like a beacon in the storm, It still sends forth its light, To make the pathway bright. The dead in Christ and we remaining, shall be upward caught; Oh, what a day 'twill be, Blest day of victory!

Chorus

The Christ I love is coming soon. It may be morning, night or noon;

Ritard.

My lamps are lit, I'll watch and pray; It may be to-day, it may be to-day.

Copyright 1950 by Beatrice Bush Bixler. Assigned to Singspiration, Inc. All rights reserved

MANSION OVER THE HILLTOP

I. S.
IRA STANPHILL

1. I'm sat-is-fied with just a cot-tage be-low, A lit-tle sil-ver and a lit-tle gold; But in that cit-y where the ransomed will shine, I want a gold one that's sil-ver lined.
2. Tho' oft-en tempt-ed, tor-ment-ed and test-ed And like the proph-et my pil-low a stone; And tho I find here no per-ma-nent dwell-ing, I know He'll give me a mansion my own.
3. Don't think me poor or de-sert-ed or lone-ly, I'm not dis-cour-aged, I'm heav-en bound; I'm just a pil-grim in search of a cit-y, I want a man-sion, a harp and a crown.

Chorus

I've got a man-sion just o-ver the hill-top, In that bright land where we'll nev-er grow old; And some day yon-der we will nev-er more wan-der But walk the streets that are pur-est gold.

Copyright 1949 by Singspiration, Inc. All rights reserved.

20. I WAS THERE WHEN IT HAPPENED

COPYRIGHT 1920, RENEWAL 1948
THE RODEHEAVER CO., OWNER

H. J. L.
HERBERT J. LACEY

1. You ask me how I know that Je-sus saves me, How I know that all my sins are white as snow; You ask me how I know that He for-gave me; Now lis-ten, I must tell you how I know.
2. You ask me how I know that He re-deemed me; And how I re-ceived the peace no gold can buy; How from the guilt and pow'r of sin He saved me, Made me an heir to man-sions in the sky.
3. And now, as thru the world I go re-joic-ing, I am tell-ing what a Sav-ior dwells with-in; How I plunged in-to the cleans-ing, crim-son foun-tain, And Je-sus washed my soul from ev-'ry sin.

Chorus

I was there when it hap-pened, and I ought to know; His Spir-it burn-ing in me, set my heart a-glow; So I praise the Lord to-day, He has

I WAS THERE WHEN IT HAPPENED

washed my sins a-way; I was there when it hap-pened, and I ought to know.

IT TOOK A MIRACLE 21

J. W. P.
JOHN W. PETERSON

1. My Fa-ther is om-ni-po-tent, And that you can't de-ny; A God of might and
2. Though here His glory has been shown, We still can't ful-ly see; The won-ders of His
3. The Bi-ble tells us of His pow'r, And wis-dom all way through; And ev-'ry lit-tle

Chorus

mir-a-cles, 'Tis writ-ten in the sky.
might—His throne, 'Twill take e-ter-ni-ty! It took a mir-a-cle to put the
bird and flow'r, Are tes-ti-mo-nies, too.

stars in place, It took a mir-a-cle to hang the world in space; But when He

saved my soul, Cleansed and made me whole, It took a mir-a-cle of love and grace!

COPYRIGHT 1948 BY PERCY B. CRAWFORD
PUBLISHED BY HILL AND RANGE SONGS, INC., NEW YORK, N. Y.
BY ARRANGEMENT WITH YOUNG PEOPLES CHURCH OF THE AIR INC
INTERNATIONAL COPYRIGHT SECURED
USED BY PERMISSION

22 THE BREAKING OF THE BREAD

Inscribed to Mrs. J. J. Van Hine, French Indo-China.

B. B. B.   BEATRICE BUSH BIXLER

1. A-long the shores of Gal-i-lee, When Christ five thou-sand fed
2. Long years have passed and few have heard That Je-sus Christ has bled, That
3. Great God, Who gave Thine on-ly Son, Help us, now Spir-it led, To

Not one was o-mit-ted In the break-ing of the bread. To-
they might feed on Him Who died To be that Liv-ing Bread. To
tell the sto-ry of Thy love To those who ask for bread. Then

day they die in hea-then lands, They die in want and dread, For
gods of stone and wood they cry, Yet they are nev-er fed For
glad-ly will we go or send, Till this blest news has spread, And

they have been o-mit-ted in the break-ing of the Bread.
they have been o-mit-ted in the break-ing of the Bread.
they have been in-clud-ed in the break-ing of the Bread.

Chorus

Lord, I would give them the Bread of Life, The Liv-ing Wa-ter too;

THE BREAKING OF THE BREAD

My heart cries out "Oh, here am I, Read-y, Thy will to do."

Copyright 1944 by Beatrice Bush Bixler. Assigned to Singspiration, Inc. All rights reserved.

THANK YOU, LORD   23

Hebrews xiii. 15   I Thes. v. 18

Mr. and Mrs. S. S.   Mr. and Mrs. SETH SYKES

1. Some thank the Lord for friends and home, For mer-cies sure and sweet; But I would praise Him for His grace, In prayer I would re-peat.
2. Some thank Him for the flow'rs that grow, Some for the stars that shine; My heart is filled with joy and praise, Be-cause I know He's mine.
3. I trust in Him from day to day, I prove His sav-ing grace; I'll sing this song of praise to Him, Un-til I see His face.

Chorus

Thank you Lord, for sav-ing my soul; Thank you Lord, for mak-ing me whole; Thank you, Lord, for giv-ing to me Thy great sal-va-tion so rich and free.

Copyright 1940. Renewal 1968 by Mrs. Seth Sykes. Assigned to Singspiration, Inc.
Verses and music Arr. Copyright 1945 by Singspiration, Inc. All rights reserved.

24 — I AM NOT WORTHY

B. B. B.
BEATRICE BUSH BIXLER

1. I am not wor-thy the least of His fa-vor, But Jesus left Heaven for me. The Word became flesh and He died as my Sav-iour, For-sak-en on dark Cal-va-ry.
2. I am not wor-thy the least of His fa-vor, But "in the Be-lov-ed" I stand; Now I'm an heir with my won-der-ful Sav-iour, And all things are mine at His hand.
3. I am not wor-thy the least of His fa-vor, But He is pre-par-ing a place Where I shall dwell with my glo-ri-fied Sav-iour, For-ev-er to look on His face.

Chorus

I am not wor-thy! This dull tongue re-peats it; I am not wor-thy! This heart glad-ly beats it. Je-sus left Heav-en to die in my place—What mer-cy, What love and what grace!

Copyright 1949 by Beatrice Bush Bixler. Assigned to Singspiration, Inc. All rights reserved.

HE BROUGHT THE SUNLIGHT TO ME   25

S. E. C.   Sidney E. Cox

1. One hap-py day in-to this low-ly dwell-ing My Sav-iour came with a par-don for me; He gave me joy, all my dark-ness dis-pel-ling, His smile of love brought the sun-light to me.
2. Oft would my sin and my way-ward-ness grieve Him, Self-seek-ing ways of fol-ly were mine; In wil-ful ways would my stray-ing feet leave Him. Yet on my path-way His love-light did shine.
3. Thru' dark-ened days, and by roads that are wind-ing, Dan-gers may threat-en and fierce winds may blow; While I press on-ward His sun-light I'm find-ing Shines all the bright-er the far-ther I go.

Chorus

He brought the sun-light to me; (to me;) He brought the sun-light to me; (to me;) When in my sin, Dark-ness with-in, He brought the sun-light to me. (to me.)

© 1956 by Alfred B. Smith. Assigned to Singspiration, Inc. All rights reserved.

PEACE IN THE VALLEY

Words and Music by
THOMAS A. DORSEY

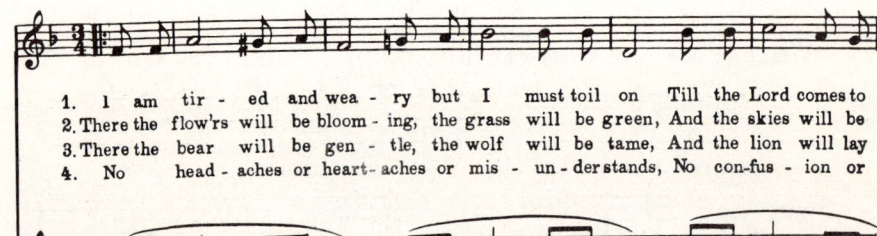

Moderato

1. I am tir-ed and wea-ry but I must toil on Till the Lord comes to
2. There the flow'rs will be bloom-ing, the grass will be green, And the skies will be
3. There the bear will be gen-tle, the wolf will be tame, And the lion will lay
4. No head-aches or heart-aches or mis-un-derstands, No con-fus-ion or

call me a - way   Where the morn - ing is bright   and the
clear and se - rene,   The sun ev - er shines, giv - ing
down by the Lamb   The host from the wild will be
trou - ble won't be,   No frowns to de - file   just a

Copyright 1939 by Thomas A. Dorsey, Chicago, Illinois
Copyright assigned 1951 to HILL AND RANGE SONGS, INC. New York, N. Y.
International Copyright Secured   Printed in U.S.A.
All rights reserved including the right of public performance for profit.

PEACE IN THE VALLEY

Lamb is the light And the night is as fair as the day.
one end-less beam And no clouds there will ev-er be seen.
led by a Child, I'll be changed from the crea-ture I am.
big end-less smile, There'll be peace and con-tent-ment for me.

CHORUS

There'll be peace in the val-ley for me some-day, There'll be peace in the val-ley for me. I pray no more sor-row and sad-ness or trou-ble will be, There'll be peace in the val-ley for me. me.

27 AT THE FOOT OF THE OLD RUGGED CROSS

J. W. P.
John W. Peterson

1. There's a place where sin's for - giv - en, Where there's cleansing from guilt' and from dross; There's a road that starts for Heav - en—At the foot of the old rug - ged cross.
2. There's a place where cares are lift - ed, Cares and bur - dens that bring one but loss; There's a place where clouds are rift - ed—At the foot of the old rug - ged cross.
3. There's a place of peace and gladness, Nev - er found in earth's glit - ter and gloss; Where there's sweet re-lease from sad - ness—At the foot of the old rug - ged cross.

CHORUS.

At the foot of the old rug - ged cross, There's an an - swer for all of your loss; And you'll find a friend - ly wel-come— At the foot of the old rug - ged cross.

© 1956 by Alfred B. Smith. Assigned to Singspiration, Inc. All rights reserved.

BY AND BY WHEN JESUS COMES

28

A. A. L.
A. A. Luther

1. When the Sav-iour went a-way, An-gels said to men:
2. He shall come with all His host, We shall meet Him then,
3. Long the church has tar-ried here, Watch-ing, pray-ing, "When?"
4. Look up, Chris-tian, dry your tears, Come, dear Lord, a-men!

"E-ven as He goes to-day, He shall come a-gain."
Be with those we've loved and lost When He comes a-gain.
They shall know that He is near, Com-ing back a-gain.
Get you read-y, calm your fears, Soon He'll come a-gain.

CHORUS

By and by when Je-sus comes To re-ceive His own, We shall meet Him in the air, See Him on His throne. La-bors end-ed, sor-rows past, Safe at home with Him at last; By and by when Je-sus comes a-gain.

Copyright 1937. Renewal 1965 by Mrs. A. A. Luther. Assigned to Singspiration, Inc. All rights reserved.

29. JESUS WON MY HEART

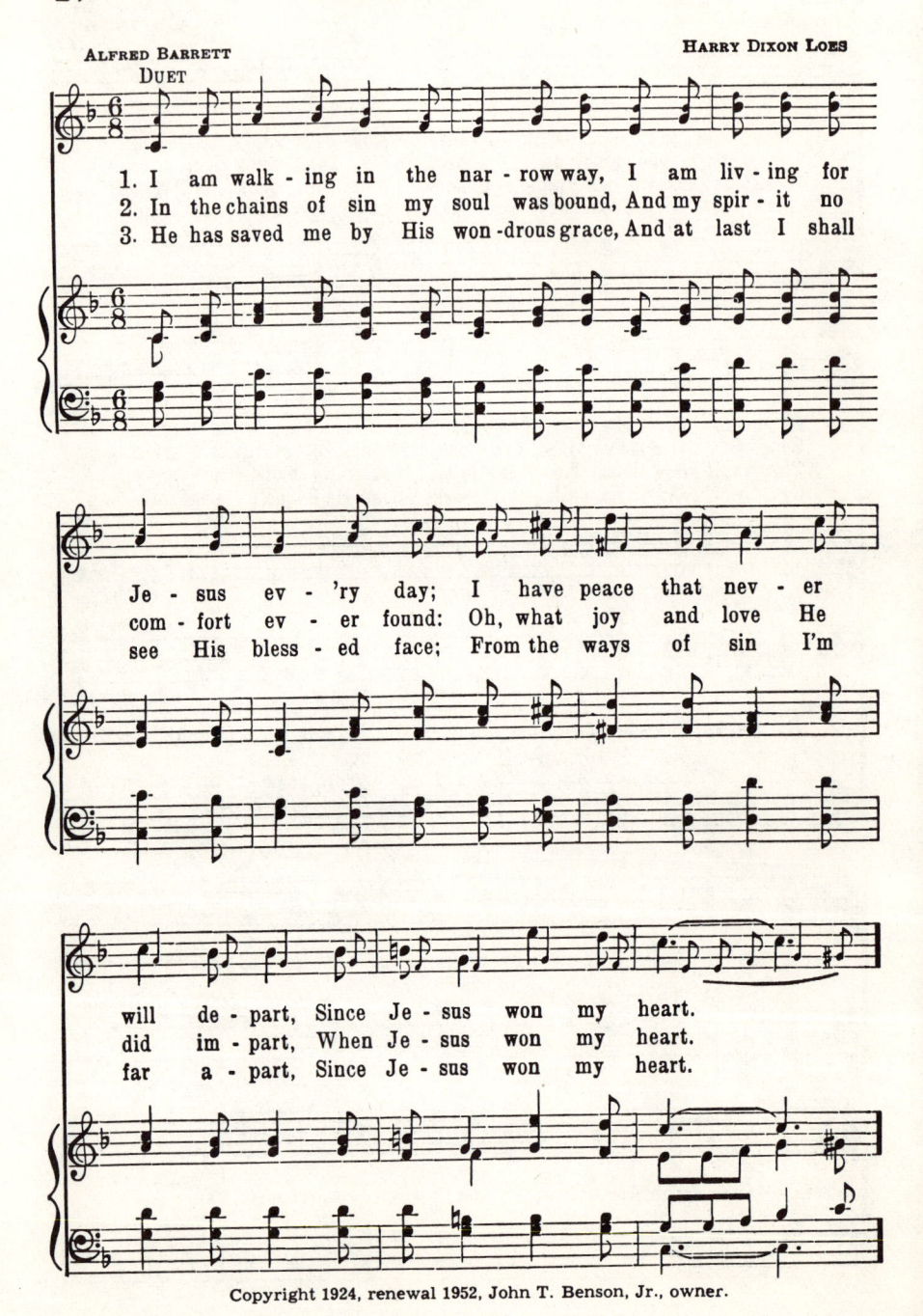

Alfred Barrett
Harry Dixon Loes

1. I am walk-ing in the nar-row way, I am liv-ing for Je-sus ev-'ry day; I have peace that nev-er will de-part, Since Je-sus won my heart.
2. In the chains of sin my soul was bound, And my spir-it no com-fort ev-er found: Oh, what joy and love He did im-part, When Je-sus won my heart.
3. He has saved me by His won-drous grace, And at last I shall see His bless-ed face; From the ways of sin I'm far a-part, Since Je-sus won my heart.

Copyright 1924, renewal 1952, John T. Benson, Jr., owner.

JESUS WON MY HEART

CHORUS

Je-sus won my heart, Je-sus won my heart; By His love so
He won my heart, He won my heart;

full and free, And the grace He gave to me. Je-sus won my heart,
He won my

Je-sus won my heart; By His love so full and free, Je-sus won my heart.
heart, He won my heart;

ad lib.

HOW GREATLY JESUS MUST HAVE LOVED ME 30

J. W. Y.   Rev. J. W. Young

How great-ly Je-sus must have loved me, How greatly Jesus must have loved me,

To bear my sins, To bear my sins In His Bod-y on the Tree!

FROM "NEW ADVENT HYMNS AND CHORUSES,"

31 GREAT IS THY NEVER-FAILING KINDNESS

© COPYRIGHT 1936. RENEWED 1964 BY THE RODEHEAVER CO., OWNER.
INTERNATIONAL COPYRIGHT SECURED.
ALL RIGHTS RESERVED.

CHAS. H. GABRIEL.   B. D. ACKLEY
SOLO OR DUET.

1. Great is Thy nev-er-fail-ing kind-ness, To us, O Lord from day to day, Lead-ing us safe-ly in our blind-ness, Re-claim-ing when we go a-stray.
2. With heav'n-ly man-na Thou hast fed us, Through sun and shade, thro' weal and woe; In pleas-ant pas-tures safe-ly led us, And where the cool-ing wa-ters flow.
3. Now as the shad-ows deep have found us, And we from toil would sink to rest, O may Thy mer-cy still sur-round us, That we may sleep su-preme-ly blest.

CHORUS

All thro' the night be ev-er near us; Thro' rest-less hours support and cheer us; Give ear, O Lord, in mer-cy hear us, To Thee a-gain we pray.
(*Last time.*) We pray a-gain, A-men.

THE CROSS IS NOT GREATER

Com. Ballington Booth
Arr. by W. J. K.

May be sung as a Solo and Chorus

1. The Cross that He gave may be heav-y, But it ne'er out-weighs His grace;
2. The thorns in my path are not sharper Than composed His crown for me;
3. The light of His love shin-eth brighter, As it falls on paths of woe;
4. His will I have joy in ful-fill-ing, As I'm walk-ing in His sight;

The storm that I feared may surround me, But it ne'er ex-cludes His face.
The cup that I drink not more bit-ter Than He drank in Geth-sem-a-ne.
The toil of my work grow-eth light-er, As I stoop to raise the low.
My all to the blood I am bring-ing, It a-lone can keep me right.

CHORUS

The Cross is not great-er than His Grace, The storm can-not hide His bless-ed face; I am sat-is-fied to know That with Je-sus here be-low, I can con-quer ev-'ry foe.

33 THEY ARE BURIED IN THE DEEP, DEEP SEA

T. O. Chisholm
Bass Solo

Merrill Dunlop

1. All my sins, which were man-y, now are gone, gone for-ev-er; I have looked to find a sin-gle one in vain; Thro' the in-fi-nite mer-cy of a dy-ing Re-deem-er, They can nev-er, nev-er trou-ble me a-gain.
2. Oh! my sins were so heav-y till His torn hands removed them, As the east is from the west, so far a-way; In the fath-om-less o-cean of His love and for-give-ness Did He bur-y them for-ev-er and for aye.
3. They are gone! Hal-le-lu-jah! There is no con-dem-na-tion; With-out fear I look in-to my Fa-ther's face; All the dark-ness has vanished and my soul is re-joic-ing In the rich-es and the won-ders of His grace.

Refrain

They are bur-ied in the deep, deep sea; They can

ad lib.

nev-er, nev-er trou-ble me! Cease, my un-a-vail-ing tears For my

Copyright 1941. Renewal 1969 by Merrill Dunlop. Assigned to Singspiration, Inc.
All rights reserved.

THEY ARE BURIED IN THE DEEP, DEEP SEA

sins of all the years,—They lie bur-ied in the deep, deep sea.

SOMEBODY'S WAITING 34

Mrs. H. S. L.   Mrs. H. S. Lehman

1. Mil-lions the sto-ry have nev-er heard, Mil-lions for whom Christ died;
2. Oh, when you look un-to Him and pray, "Fa-ther, Thy will be done,"
3. Time is fast hast'ning and sin's dark night Soon will ob-scure the way,

Lost, with-out Je-sus, be-cause the Word They have been long de-nied.
Will He not an-swer, "With-out de-lay Res-cue these hope-less ones?"
Quick-ly then car-ry the Word of Light, While it is called to-day.

CHORUS

Some-bod-y's dy-ing a-way out there, Some-bod-y needs you for earn-est pray'r;

Some-bod-y's wait-ing for you to bear The mes-sage of life in Je-sus.

Copyright 1923. Renewal 1951 by Mrs. K. Lehman Gottschling.
Assigned to Singspiration, Inc. All rights reserved.

35 WHEN I'M WITH HIM

A. H. A.
A. H. Ackley

© COPYRIGHT 1939. RENEWED 1967 BY THE RODEHEAVER CO., OWNER.
INTERNATIONAL COPYRIGHT SECURED. ALL RIGHTS RESERVED.

1. A bless-ed fel-low-ship my soul has found With Him whose sweetest name is Love;
2. I feel the ten-der touch of His dear hand, His voice so gen-tle bids me stay;
3. God's children cannot live from Him a-part, To un-der-stand, they are so slow;
4. Would you experience what I know is true? Then come to Him, with Him a-bide,

1. In Christ the rich-es of God's grace a-bound, The joys e-ter-nal from a-bove.
2. And when I fol-low His di-vine com-mand, The doubts that trou-ble pass a-way.
3. He seeks the way-ward, with a bro-ken heart, As in the days of long a-go.
4. For He is wait-ing e-ven now for you, To dwell for-ev-er at His side.

rit.

REFRAIN

When I'm with Him, . . . when I'm with Him, . . . The fair-est pleas-ures of the world grow dim; . . . And in my heart I feel the thrill of glo-ry, When I'm with Him, when I'm with Him. . . .

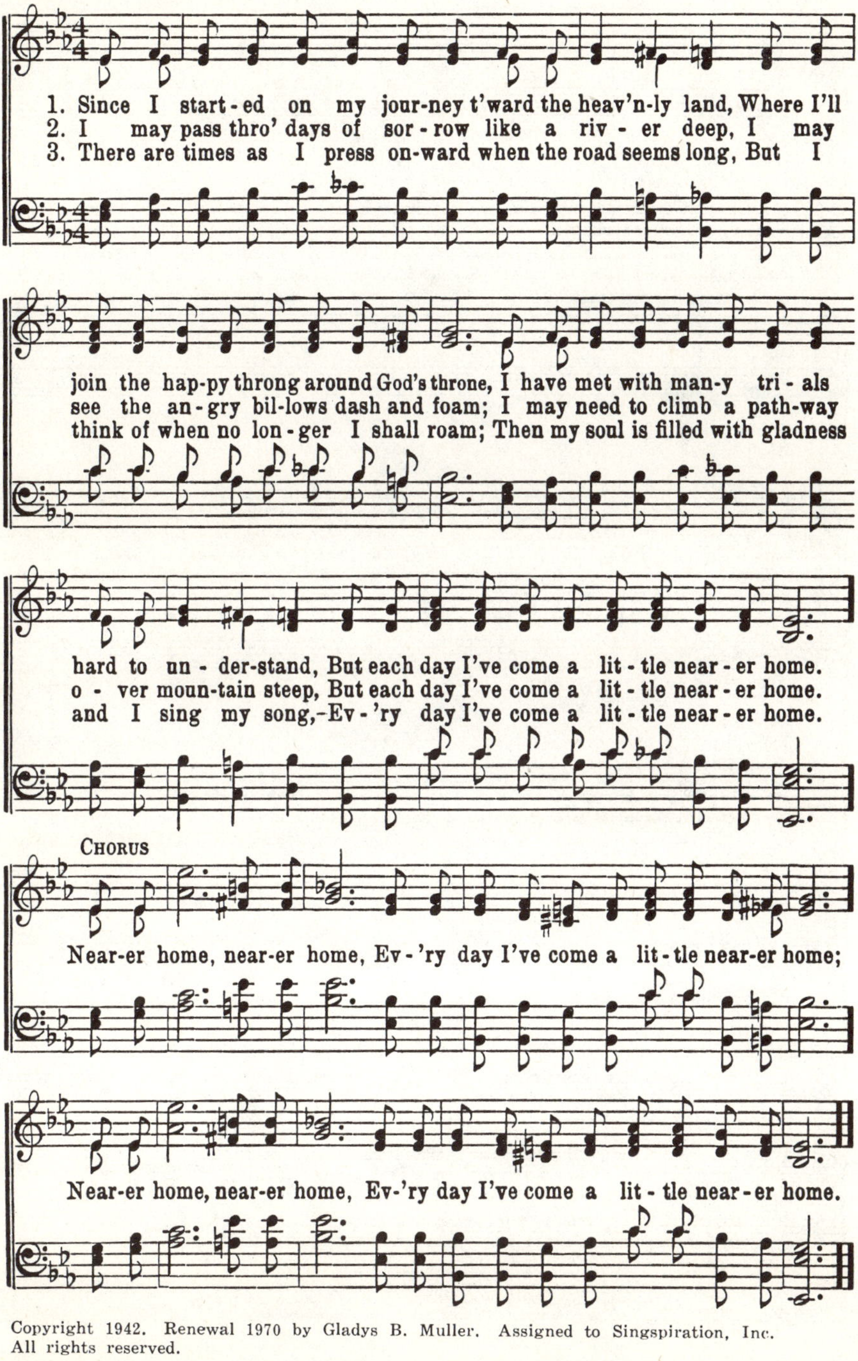

37 IS HE SATISFIED?

Words and Music by
STUART HAMBLEN

Moderately

VERSE

1. Do you ev-er search your heart as you watch the day de-part? Is there some-thing 'way down
2. (Fee-ble) is the lamp of fame by which man in-scribes his name on the walls of time for

deep you try to hide? _____ If this day should be the end and e-
oth-er men to see. _____ Though he boasts of wealth and pow'r none can

ter-ni-ty be-gin, when the book is o-pened wide, would the Lord be sat-is-fied?
help him in that hour when the an-gels hear his plea; is He sat-is-fied with me?

CHORUS

Is He sat-is-fied, is He sat-is-fied? Is He sat-is-fied with

Copyright 1951 by Hamblen Music Co.
Copyright assigned 1952 to **HILL AND RANGE SONGS, INC.,** New York, N. Y.
International Copyright Secured   Printed in U.S.A.
All rights reserved including the right of public performance for profit.

IS HE SATISFIED?

38   HIDING IN HIS LOVE

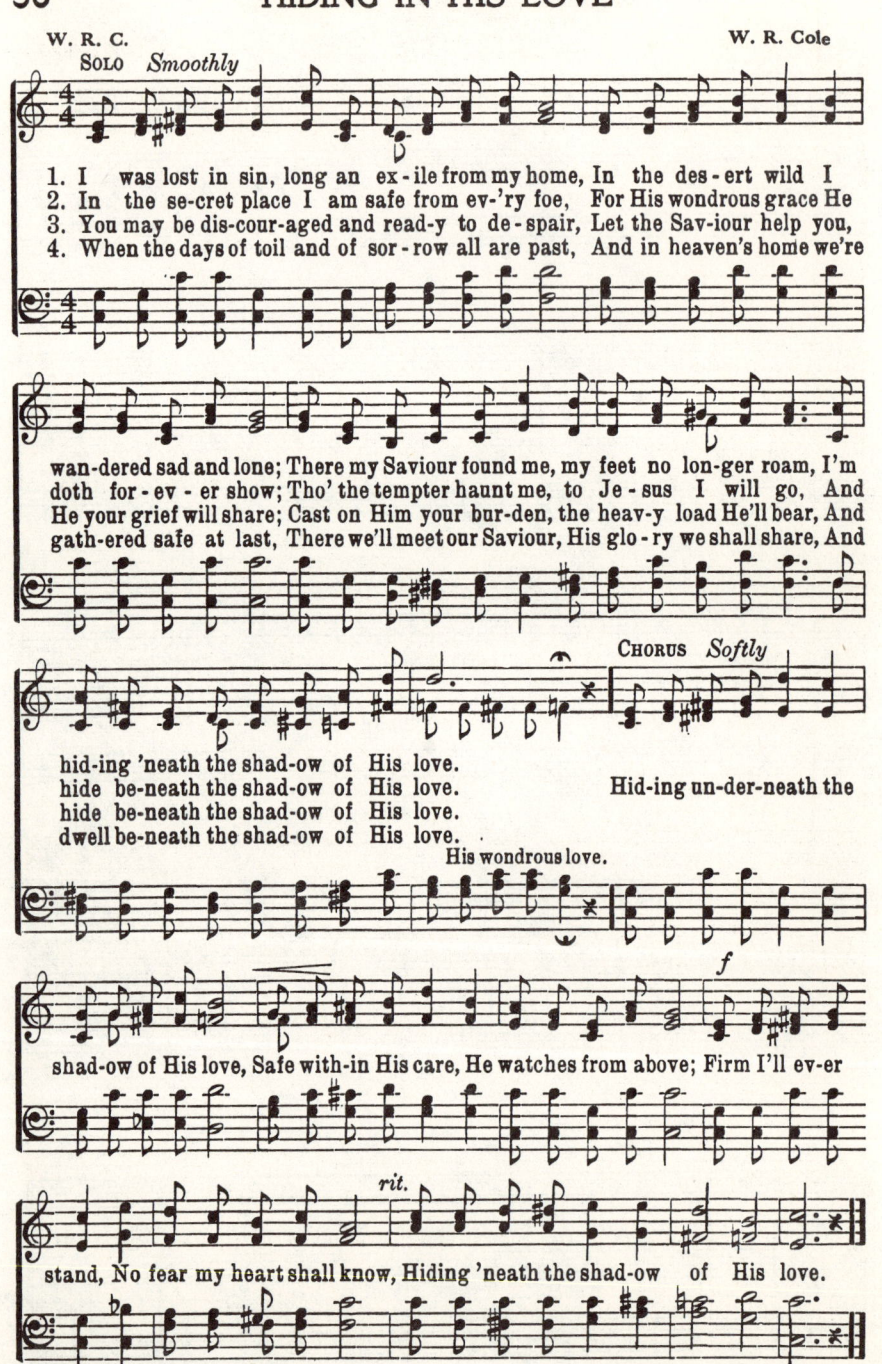

W. R. C.
W. R. Cole

SOLO *Smoothly*

1. I was lost in sin, long an ex-ile from my home, In the des-ert wild I
2. In the se-cret place I am safe from ev-'ry foe, For His wondrous grace He
3. You may be dis-cour-aged and read-y to de-spair, Let the Sav-iour help you,
4. When the days of toil and of sor-row all are past, And in heaven's home we're

wan-dered sad and lone; There my Saviour found me, my feet no lon-ger roam, I'm
doth for-ev-er show; Tho' the tempter haunt me, to Je-sus I will go, And
heav-y grief will share; Cast on Him your bur-den, the heav-y load He'll bear, And
gath-ered safe at last, There we'll meet our Saviour, His glo-ry we shall share, And

CHORUS *Softly*

hid-ing 'neath the shad-ow of His love.
hide be-neath the shad-ow of His love.
hide be-neath the shad-ow of His love.
dwell be-neath the shad-ow of His love.

Hid-ing un-der-neath the
His wondrous love.

shad-ow of His love, Safe with-in His care, He watches from above; Firm I'll ev-er

rit.

stand, No fear my heart shall know, Hiding 'neath the shad-ow of His love.

Copyright 1926. Renewal 1954 by W. R. Cole. Assigned to Singspiration, Inc. All rights reserved.

WONDERFUL MORNING

A. H. A.
Duet

COPYRIGHT, 1930, RENEWAL, 1958
THE RODEHEAVER CO., OWNER
INTERNATIONAL COPYRIGHT SECURED

A. H. Ackley

1. Morn-ing with Je-sus when la-bor is end-ed, Some-time the dream of my heart will come true, And I shall dwell with the Sav-iour as-cend-ed, In that fair realm where we live life a-new.
2. Earth's sweetest pleasures are min-gled with sad-ness, Sun-shine and shad-ow to-geth-er are found, But in God's morn-ing of e-ter-nal glad-ness Naught shall im-pair the pure joys that a-bound.
3. Rest for the wea-ry in man-sions ce-les-tial, Peace, per-fect peace for the chil-dren of light, Free-dom for-ev-er from bur-dens ter-res-trial, All shall be mine in that morn-ing so bright.

Refrain

Won-der-ful morning, wonderful morning, With the Redeemer so long I've adored, Won-der-ful morning, wonderful morning, Wonderful morning with Jesus my Lord.

40 ALL DAY LONG MY HEART KEEPS SINGING

M. D.
MERRILL DUNLOP

1. Mu-sic in my heart is ring-ing, Mel-o-dies di-vine;
2. Sor-row now has changed to bless-ing, Darkness turned to light;
3. Christ is tru-ly mine for-ev-er, Sav-ior, Lord, and Guide;

Of God's love my soul is sing-ing For His love is mine.
Since I came my sin con-fess-ing Blind-ness now is sight.
Doubts and fears can reach me nev-er When in Him I hide.

CHORUS

All day long my heart keeps sing-ing, For I know that Christ is mine;

rit.

I am now a new cre-a-tion, For I've tast-ed His sal-va-tion.

a tempo

Gone my fears, and gone my doubt-ing, I am saved by grace di-vine.

Copyright 1947 by Merrill Dunlop. Assigned to Singspiration, Inc. All rights reserved.

PRECIOUS MEMORIES

41

J. B. F. Wright

1. Precious mem-'ries, un-seen an-gels, Sent from somewhere to my soul; (to my soul;) How they lin-ger, ev-er near me, And the sa-cred past un-fold. (un-fold.)
2. Precious fa-ther, lov-ing moth-er, Fly a-cross the lone-ly years; (lonely years;) And old home scenes of my child-hood, In fond mem-o-ry ap-pears. (ap-pears.)
3. In the still-ness of the mid-night, Ech-oes from the past I hear (past I hear;) Old time-sing-ing, gladness bring-ing, From that love-ly land somewhere. (somewhere.)
4. As I trav-el on life's path-way, Know not what the years may hold; (years may hold;) As I pon-der, hope grows fon-der, Precious mem'ries flood my soul. (my soul.)

CHORUS

Pre-cious mem-'ries, how they lin-ger, How they ev-er flood my soul. In the still-ness of the mid-night, Precious, sa-cred scenes unfold. (unfold.) Precious, sa-cred scenes un-fold.

pp Slowly Use after final chorus
hum

© 1956 by Alfred B. Smith. Assigned to Singspiration, Inc. All rights reserved.

TELL JESUS

J. W. P.
John W. Peterson

1. When the way is dark be-fore you, And the path is hid from view;
2. When your heart is near-ly break-ing With a crush-ing weight of woe,
3. When with sin and self you strug-gle And you long for vic-to-ry,

When you grope with steps un-cer-tain And you know not what to do.
When you seem a-lone, for-sak-en By the earth-ly friends you know.
When you lack of pow'r for ser-vice And no last-ing fruit you see.

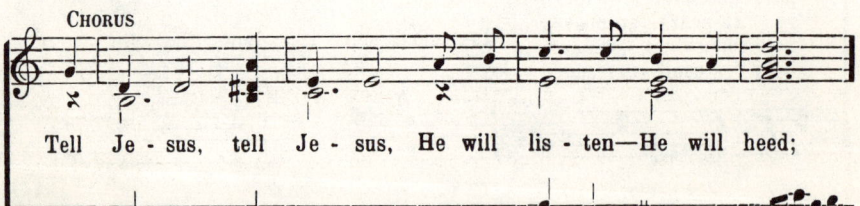

CHORUS

Tell Je-sus, tell Je-sus, He will lis-ten—He will heed;
Tell Je-sus, bless-ed Je-sus, He has grace to meet your need.

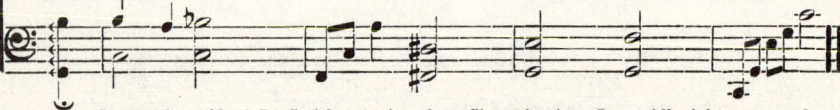

© 1956 by Alfred B. Smith. Assigned to Singspiration, Inc. All rights reserved.

HE KNOWS THE WAY

COPYRIGHT 1913, RENEWAL 1941
THE RODEHEAVER CO., OWNER

A. H. A.
A. H. Ackley

1. There is a Guide that nev-er fal-ters, And when He leads I can-not stray
2. Oft-times the path grows dim and drear-y, The darkness hides the cheering ray,
3. He knows the e-vils that surround me, The turnings that would lead a-stray,
4. O heart weigh'd down with nameless anguish, O guilt-y soul torn with dis-may,

For step by step, He goes be-fore me, And marks my path, He knows the way.
Still I will trust tho' worn and wea-ry, My Sav-ior leads, He knows the way.
No foes of night can ere confound me, For Je-sus leads, He knows the way.
Thine ev-'ry foe, His pow'r will vanquish, Let Je-sus lead, He knows the way.

Chorus

He knows the way that leads to glo-ry; Thy ev-'ry fear He will al-lay,
He knows the way Thy ev-'ry fear

And bring thee safe at last to heav-en, Let Je-sus lead, He knows the way.

44 WILL THERE BE ANY STARS?

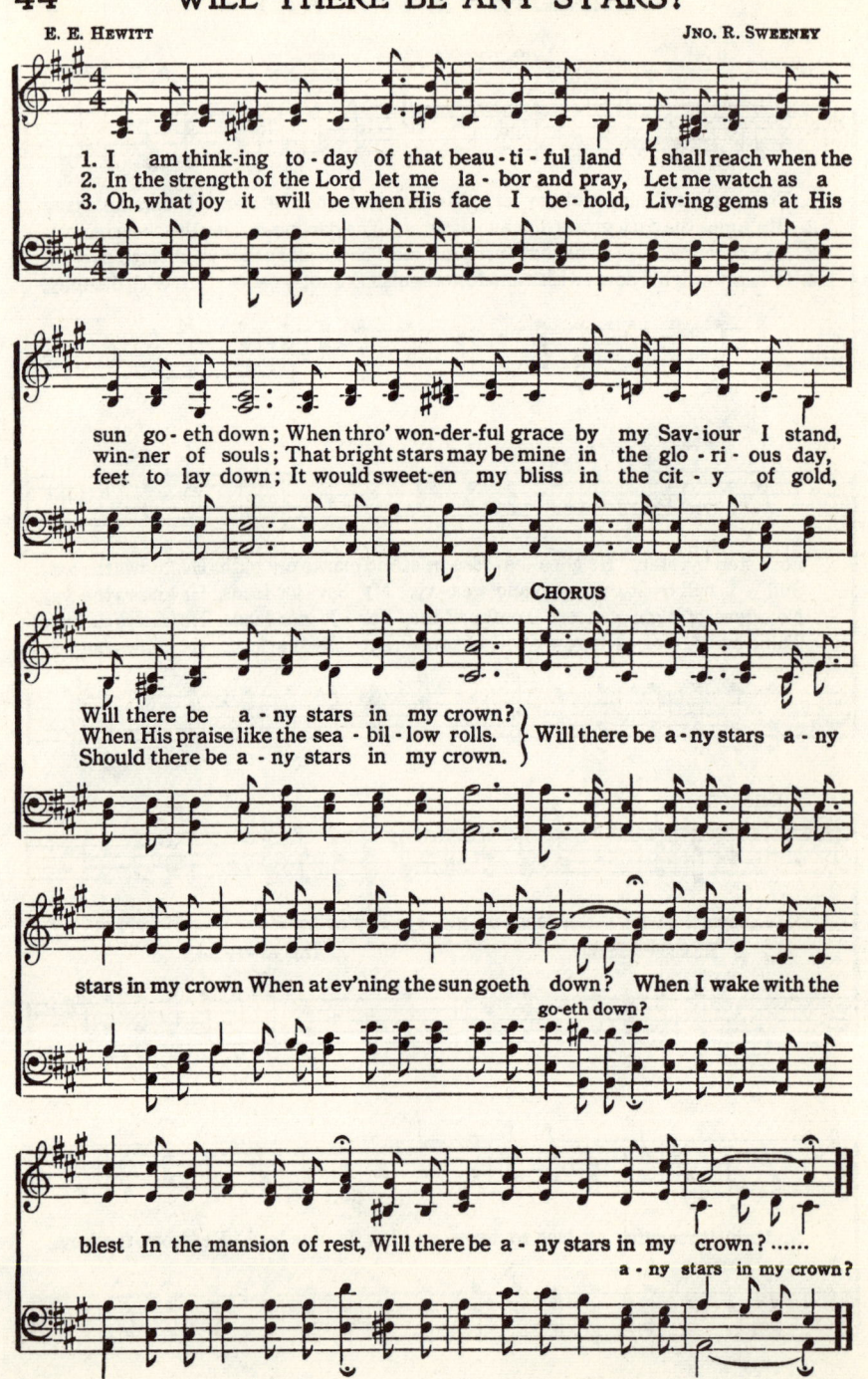

E. E. Hewitt
Jno. R. Sweeney

1. I am think-ing to-day of that beau-ti-ful land I shall reach when the
2. In the strength of the Lord let me la-bor and pray, Let me watch as a
3. Oh, what joy it will be when His face I be-hold, Liv-ing gems at His

sun go-eth down; When thro' won-der-ful grace by my Sav-iour I stand,
win-ner of souls; That bright stars may be mine in the glo-ri-ous day,
feet to lay down; It would sweet-en my bliss in the cit-y of gold,

Chorus

Will there be a-ny stars in my crown?
When His praise like the sea-bil-low rolls. } Will there be a-ny stars a-ny
Should there be a-ny stars in my crown.

stars in my crown When at ev'ning the sun goeth down? When I wake with the
go-eth down?

blest In the mansion of rest, Will there be a-ny stars in my crown?......
a-ny stars in my crown?

WHERE DREAMS COME TRUE

©COPYRIGHT 1935. RENEWED 1963 BY THE RODEHEAVER CO., OWNER.
INTERNATIONAL COPYRIGHT SECURED.
ALL RIGHTS RESERVED.

Rev. Oswald J. Smith   B. D. Ackley

Solo

1. I'm long-ing, dear Lord, for that ha-ven, Where we shall be
2. My dreams have been shat-tered, and per-ished Be-neath the rough
3. The fac-es of those who have loved me, In days of the
4. And soon will the voy-age be o-ver, The heav-en-ly

trou-bled no more, . . . Like trav-el-ers out on the o-cean . . .
waves of life's sea, . . . And yet in that calm, peaceful slumber . . .
long, long a-go, . . . Be-yond the dark wa-ters as-sure me, . . .
port come in sight, . . . And there I shall an-chor for-ev-er, . . .

Chorus

Who long for the home on the shore. . . .
I'll find their ful-fill-ment in Thee. . . . Where my dreams will come
A-gain I shall see them, I know. . . .
And dwell in the Cit-y of Light. . . .

true, . . . Where my dreams will come true; . . . The joys that I

lost in the shad-ows . . . Will be found where my dreams come true. . . .

46. THE SONG OF THE SOUL SET FREE

© COPYRIGHT 1938, RENEWED 1966 BY THE RODEHEAVER CO., OWNER
INTERNATIONAL COPYRIGHT SECURED. ALL RIGHTS RESERVED.

OSWALD J. SMITH   A. H. ACKLEY

1. Fair-est of ten thousand, Is Je-sus Christ my Sav-iour, The Lil-y of the Val-ley, The Bright and Morning Star,......... He is all my glo-ry, And in this heart of mine, For-ev-er-more I'm sing-ing, A song of love di-vine.
2. Once my heart was burdened, But now I am for-giv-en, And with a song of glad-ness, I'm on my way to heav'n;...... Christ is my Re-deem-er, My Song of songs is He, My Saviour, Lord and Master, To Him my praise shall be.
3. When He came to save me, He set the joy bells ring-ing, And now I'm ev-er sing-ing, For Christ has ransomed me;......... Once I lived in dark-ness, My light I could not see, But now I sing His prais-es, For He has set me free.
4. An-gels can-not sing it, This song of joy and free-dom, For mor-tals on-ly know it, The ransomed and the free;......... Slaves were they in bond-age, And deep-est mis-er-y, But now they sing triumphant, Their song of lib-er-ty.

CHORUS

'Tis the song of the soul set free, set free, And its mel-o-dy is ring-ing;
'Tis the song of the soul set free, set free, Joy and peace to me it's bring-ing,

THE SONG OF THE SOUL SET FREE

'Tis the song of the soul set free, set free, And my heart is ev-er sing-ing Hal-le-lu - - jah! Hal-le-lu - - jah! The song of the soul set free.

Hal - le - lu - jah! Hal - le - lu - jah!

GOD IS GOOD

COPYRIGHT, 1926, RENEWAL, 1954
THE RODEHEAVER CO., OWNER
INTERNATIONAL COPYRIGHT SECURED

T. O. Chisholm

Chas. H. Gabriel

47

1. God is good—the heav'ns declare it— Far - off stars and beam-ing sun,
2. God is good—the earth proclaims it In a cho-rus loud and strong,
3. God is good, we soft - ly whis-per When the deep'ning shades en-fold,
4. God is good! then let us trust Him Like the lit - tle chil-dren do,

SOLO. *Bass*

Wit - ness-ing to hearts that lis - ten In a language all their own.
Birds and flow - ers, fields and woodlands Join - ing in the trib - ute song.
E - ven 'mid life's pain and sor - row We His goodness may be - hold.
He hath giv - en to His an - gels Charge concerning me and you.

MY GOD IS REAL
(YES, GOD IS REAL)

Words and Music by
KENNETH MORRIS

Slowly

VERSE

1. There are some things I may not know; there are some plac-es I can't go, But I am sure of this one thing: that God is real for I can feel Him deep with-in.
2. (Some folks may) doubt some folks may scorn; all can de-sert and leave me a-lone. But as for me I'll take God's part, for God is real and I can feel Him in my heart.
3. (I can-not) tell just how you felt when Je-sus took your sins a-way. But since that day, yes, since that hour, God has been real for I can feel His ho-ly power.

Copyright 1944 by Kenneth Morris
Published by HILL AND RANGE SONGS, INC., New York, N.Y. by arrangement with Martin and Morris Music Studio, Inc.
International Copyright Secured Printed in U.S.A.
All rights reserved including the right of public performance for profit.

MY GOD IS REAL

CHORUS

My God is real, real in my soul; My God is real for He has washed and made me whole. His love for me is like pure gold. My God is real for I can feel Him in my soul.

2. Some folks may
3. I can - not

49 PASS IT ON

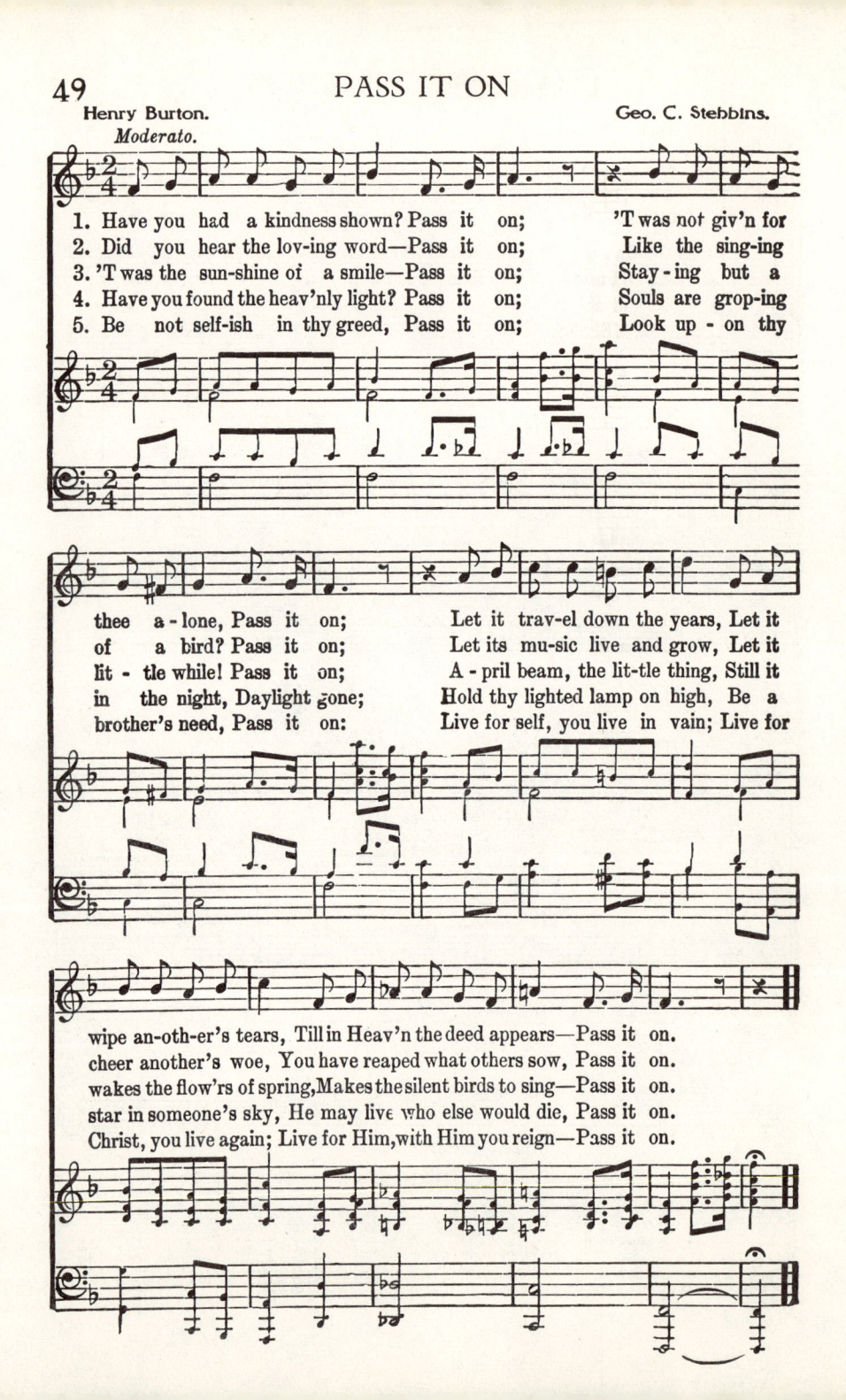

Henry Burton.
Geo. C. Stebbins.
Moderato.

1. Have you had a kindness shown? Pass it on; 'Twas not giv'n for thee a-lone, Pass it on; Let it trav-el down the years, Let it wipe an-oth-er's tears, Till in Heav'n the deed appears—Pass it on.
2. Did you hear the lov-ing word—Pass it on; Like the sing-ing of a bird? Pass it on; Let its mu-sic live and grow, Let it cheer another's woe, You have reaped what others sow, Pass it on.
3. 'Twas the sun-shine of a smile—Pass it on; Stay-ing but a lit-tle while! Pass it on; A-pril beam, the lit-tle thing, Still it wakes the flow'rs of spring, Makes the silent birds to sing—Pass it on.
4. Have you found the heav'nly light? Pass it on; Souls are grop-ing in the night, Daylight gone; Hold thy lighted lamp on high, Be a star in someone's sky, He may live who else would die, Pass it on.
5. Be not self-ish in thy greed, Pass it on; Look up-on thy brother's need, Pass it on: Live for self, you live in vain; Live for Christ, you live again; Live for Him, with Him you reign—Pass it on.

LORD, SEND ME THERE

N. B. Herrell.
DUET.
COPYRIGHT © 1951, BY LILLENAS PUBLISHING CO. ALL RIGHTS RESERVED
Haldor Lillenas.

1. O-ver the o-cean millions I see, Fet-tered in bond-age, beck-on-ing me, Crushed beneath sor-row too heav-y to bear; Glad-ly I an-swer,
2. Fa-thers and moth-ers lost in the night, Grop-ing in darkness, longing for light, No eye to pit-y and no one to care; Glad-ly I an-swer,
3. Brothers and sis-ters born to our race, Help-less and dy-ing, hopeless their case; Who will go win them and love's message bear? Glad-ly I an-swer,
4. Christ the chief Shepherd now leads the way, Seek-ing the lost ones far gone a-stray; He sees their weep-ing, He an-swers prayer: Glad-ly I whis-per,

D. S.—*Glad-ly I an-swer,*

FINE. REFRAIN.

Lord, send me there! Lord, send me there, O Lord, send me there; Glad-ly I an-swer, Lord, send me there! Out where the mil-lions die in de-spair,

D. S.

51. MY DEBT OF LOVE

E. Margaret Clarkson
Alfred B. Smith

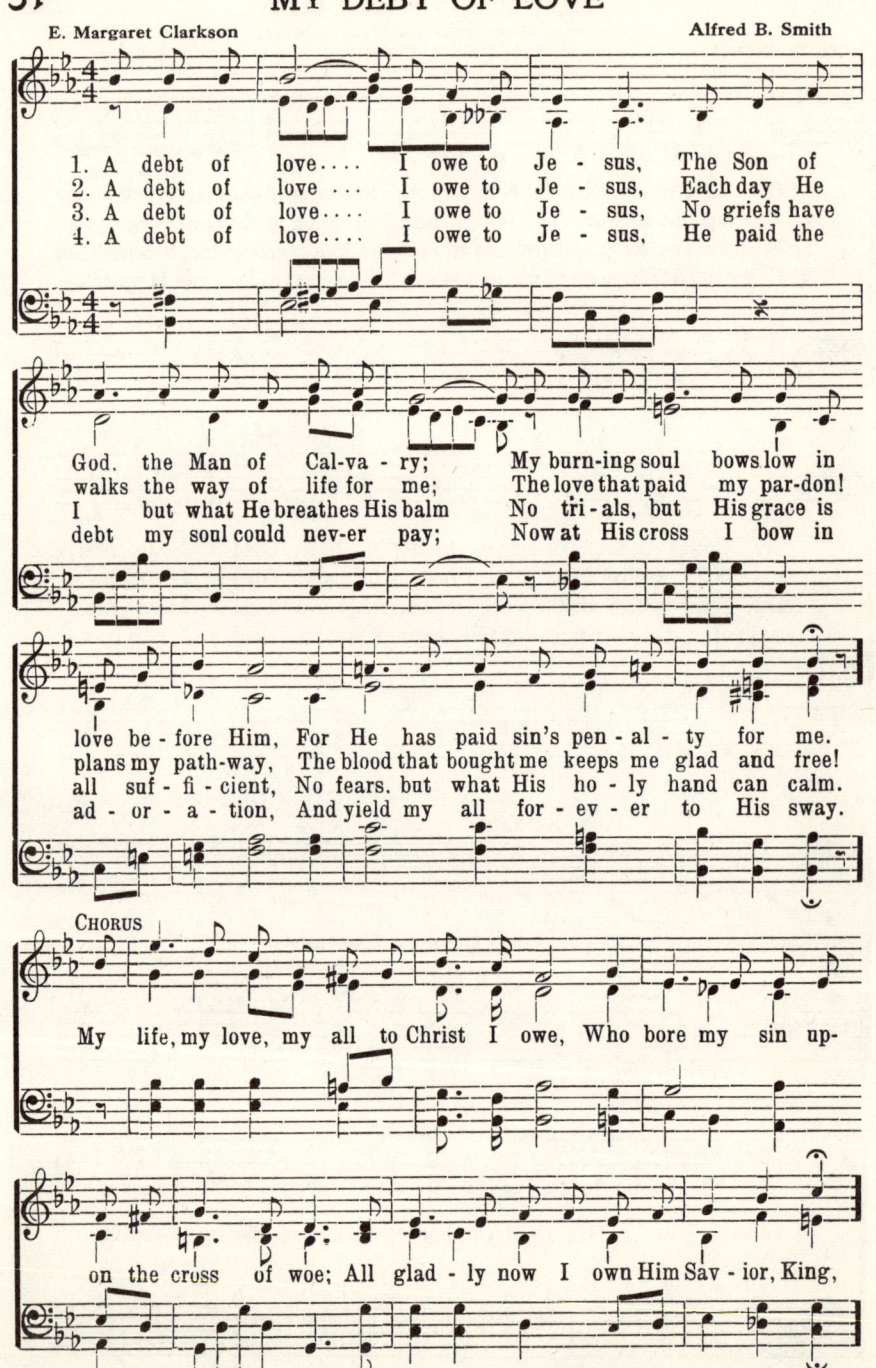

1. A debt of love.... I owe to Jesus, The Son of God, the Man of Calvary; My burning soul bows low in love before Him, For He has paid sin's penalty for me.
2. A debt of love.... I owe to Jesus, Each day He walks the way of life for me; The love that paid my pardon! plans my pathway, The blood that bought me keeps me glad and free!
3. A debt of love.... I owe to Jesus, No griefs have I but what He breathes His balm, No trials, but His grace is all sufficient, No fears, but what His holy hand can calm.
4. A debt of love.... I owe to Jesus, He paid the debt my soul could never pay; Now at His cross I bow in adoration, And yield my all forever to His sway.

Chorus

My life, my love, my all to Christ I owe, Who bore my sin upon the cross of woe; All gladly now I own Him Savior, King,

Copyright 1950 by Alfred B. Smith. Assigned to Singspiration, Inc. All rights reserved.

MY DEBT OF LOVE
(8va.....)

My debt of love to Christ I bring!

GOD IS NOT FAR AWAY 52

Alfred B. Smith and
Sidney E. Cox

S. E. C.

1. Are you sad and lone - ly? lift your heart and pray; Though the
2. God will nev - er fail you, trust in Him al - way; In the

clouds may hide the sun-shine— God is not far a - way.
hour when need is great-est— God is not far a - way.

CHORUS

Clouds will turn to sun - shine, night will turn to day;

If you'll just re - mem - ber God is not far a - way.

© 1956 by Alfred B. Smith. Assigned to Singspiration, Inc. All rights reserved.

53 KEEP ON BELIEVING

C. S. B.
Solo or duet

Arr. by John W. Peterson
C. S. Bullock

1. When thou art weak-est, tri - als a - bound, Sub-tle temp-ta-tions, trou-bles sur-round,
2. If in temp-ta - tion, then He is near; He knows thy danger, why shouldst thou fear?
3. If old companions—friends of gone days— Gath-er a-round thee, tempt to their ways,

All things seem hopeless, nothing seems glad, All is de-spair-ing, e-ven-time sad.
He will up-hold thee, cause thee to stand, Cheering thee ev - er, hold-ing thy hand.
Look to the Sav-iour, seek Him in pray'r He will pro-tect thee, nev - er des - pair.

Chorus

Keep on be - liev - ing; Je - sus is near,... Keep on be-
is near,

liev - ing, there's noth-ing to fear;.... Keep on be - liev - ing, this is the
to fear;

way,........ Faith in the night - time as well as the day.
this is the way,

© 1956 by Alfred B. Smith. Assigned to Singspiration, Inc. All rights reserved.

JESUS LED ME ALL THE WAY

J. W. P.
John W. Peterson

1. Some-day life's jour-ney will be o'er, And I shall reach that dis-tant shore,
I'll sing while en-t'ring Heaven's door—"Je-sus led me all the way."
2. If God should let me there re-view The wind-ing paths of earth I knew,
It would be prov-en clear and true— Je-sus led me all the way.
3. And hith-er-to my Lord has led, To-day He guides each step I tread,
And soon in Heav'n it will be said— Je-sus led me all the way.

Chorus

Je-sus led me all the way, Led me step by step each day; I will tell the saints and an-gels as I lay my bur-dens down "Je-sus led me all the way."

Copyright 1954 by The Moody Bible Institute. Assigned to Singspiration, Inc. All rights reserved.

55 — IN THE STILL OF THE NIGHT

H. D. L.
Harry Dixon Loes

1. In the still of the night Jesus came to me, As I listened, He whispered so tenderly: "Mourn thou not the day now gone, ... Fear thou not the coming dawn." ..... So I rolled ev-'ry care on His gentle breast, And there came to my spirit a hallowed rest; With Jesus near, I had no fear, In the still of the night. ....

2. In the still of the night is a blessed time To commune with the Lord—'tis a joy sublime! Then He closer seems to me, ... From the daily clamor free. ...... So I roll ev-'ry care on His gentle breast, And there comes to my spirit a hallowed rest; With Him so near, I have no fear, In the still of the night. ....

3. In the still of the night He will come to you, When the world is so dark, and your friends seem few; As a child, on Him then call, ... Fully trusting Him for all. ...... If you'll roll ev-'ry care on His gentle breast, He will give to your spirit a hallowed rest; With Him so near, you'll have no fear, In the still of the night. ....

Copyright 1948 by H. D. Loes. Assigned to Singspiration, Inc. All rights reserved.

LOOKING IN THE FACE OF JESUS

H. D. C.
H. D. Clarke

1. Look-ing in the face of Je - sus, Won-drous beau-ty there I see;
2. Look-ing in the face of Je - sus, There I see such ag - o - ny
3. Look-ing in the face of Je - sus, Hope and com-fort there I see,

Ten - der - ness di - vine a - bound - ing, Pur - er love there could not be.
Caused by sin - ful hands that nailed Him To that cross on Cal - va - ry.
Giv - ing me that blest as - sur - ance That He will re - turn for me.

Chorus

1. 2. Oh, I want to be more like Him So that men can plain-ly see
3. On that day I shall be like Him Clothed in im - mor - tal - i - ty,

Christ in all His wondrous beau - ty Liv-ing on, His life in me.
When I rise in His own like - ness Liv-ing on, His life in me.

Copyright 1951 by Alfred B. Smith. Assigned to Singspiration, Inc. All rights reserved.

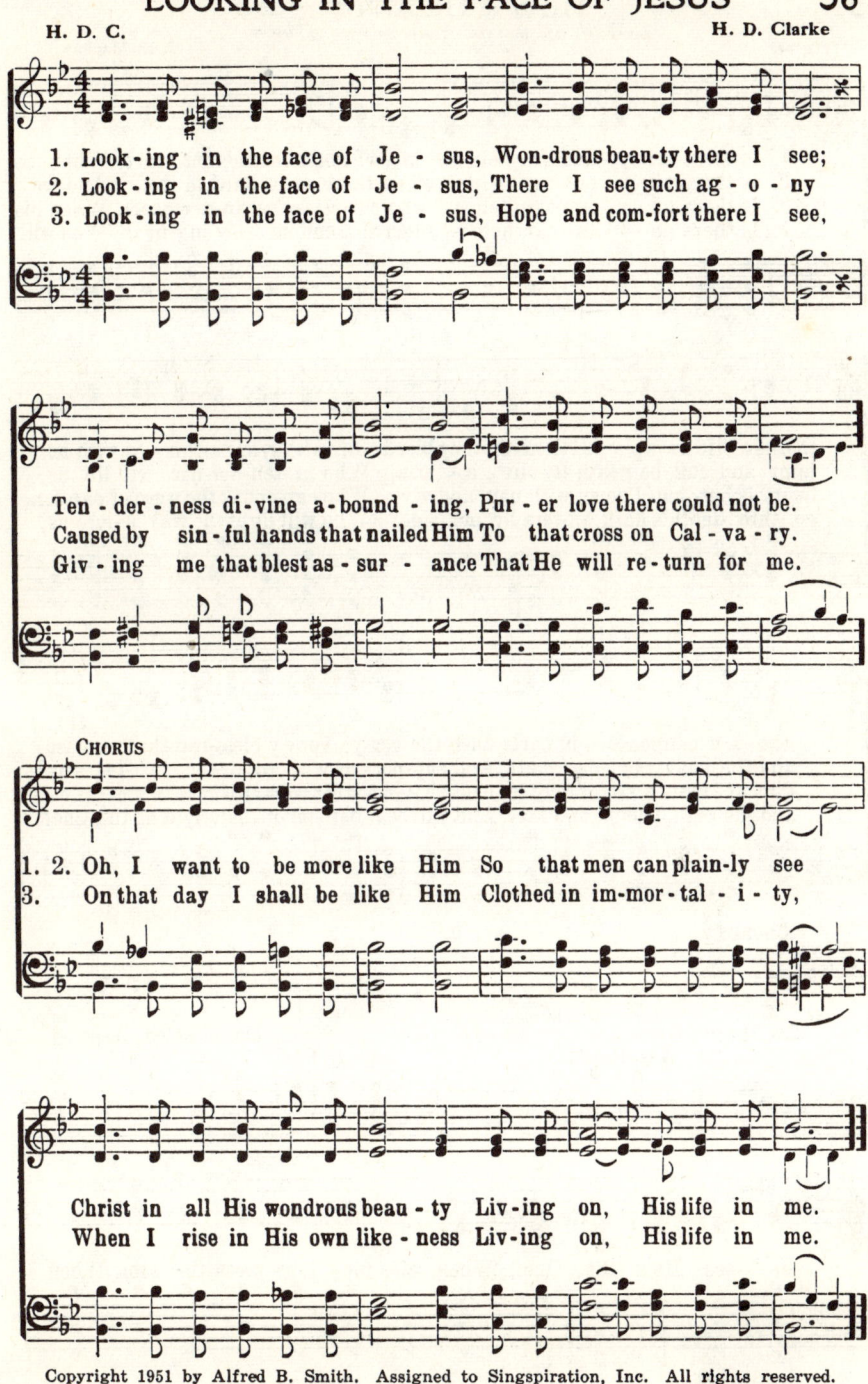

57 HE'S THE ONE

J. B. M.

COPYRIGHT, 1926, RENEWAL. THE RODEHEAVER CO., OWNER

J. B. Mackay

1. Is there an-y-one can help us—one who understands our hearts, When the
2. Is there an-y-one can help us when the load is hard to bear, And we
3. Is there an-y-one can help us who can give the sin-ner peace, When his
4. Is there an-y-one can help us when the end is draw-ing near, Who will

thorns of life have pierced them till they bleed; One who sym-pa-thiz-es with us,
faint and fall be-neath it in a-larm; Who in ten-der-ness will lift us,
heart is bur-dened down with pain and woe; Who can speak the word of par-don,
go thro' death's dark wa-ters by our side; Who will light the way be-fore us,

who in wondrous love imparts Just the ver-y, ver-y bless-ing that we need?
and the heav-y bur-den share, And sup-port us with an ev-er-last-ing arm?
that af-fords a sweet release, And whose blood can wash and make us white as snow?
and dis-pel all doubt and fear, And will bear our spir-its safe-ly o'er the tide?

CHORUS

Yes, there's One! on-ly One! The bless-ed, bless-ed
Yes, there's One, on-ly One!

Je-sus, He's the One! When af-flic-tions press the soul, When

HE'S THE ONE

...waves of troub-le roll, And you need a Friend to help you, He...

WHEN GOD SPEAKS 58

Carlton C. Buck
SOLO
Frank A. Simpkins

1. When God speaks, the high mountains tremble; When God speaks, the loud bil-lows roll;
2. When God speaks, the an-gels o-bey Him; When God speaks, all na-ture is stirred;
3. When God speaks, the sad hush their cry-ing; When God speaks, the wea-ry find rest;
4. When God speaks, 'tis mine then to an-swer; When God speaks, my tem-pest to still;

When God speaks, my heart falls to lis-t'ning, And there is re-sponse in my soul.
When God speaks, the hard hearts are soft-ened, For no sweet-er voice e'er was heard.
When God speaks in sweet tones of com-fort, With in-fin-ite peace I am blest.
When God speaks, 'tis mine then to fol-low, And fol-low-ing Him, do His will.

REFRAIN

Speak to my heart! Speak now, I pray, God of sal-va-tion, and Lord of Cre-a-tion, Oh, speak to my heart to-day!

COPYRIGHT © 1936, BY HALDOR LILLENAS
ASSIGNED TO NAZARENE PUBLISHING HOUSE
ALL RIGHTS RESERVED

SOMEONE

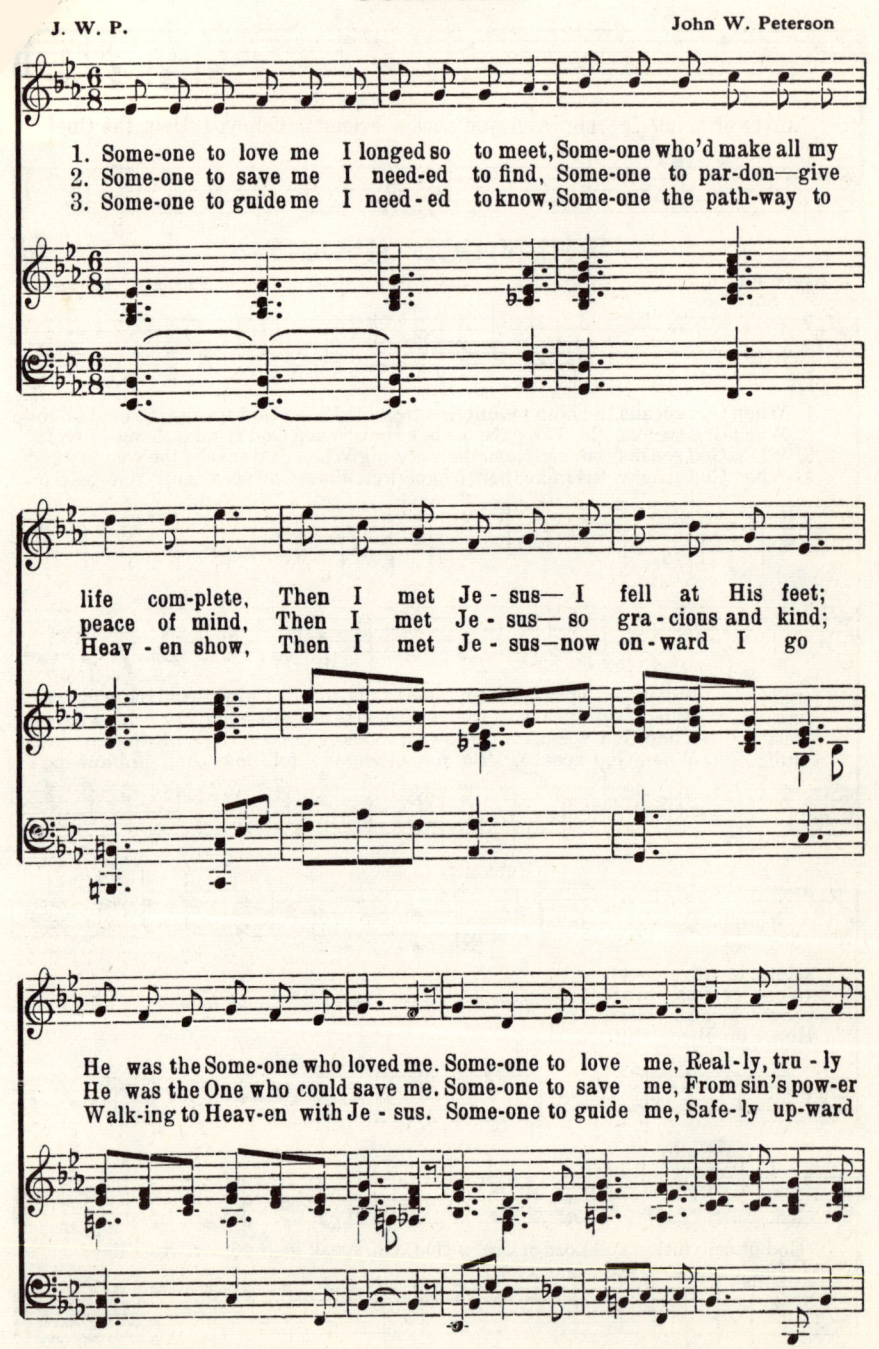

J. W. P.
John W. Peterson

1. Some-one to love me I longed so to meet, Some-one who'd make all my
2. Some-one to save me I need-ed to find, Some-one to par-don—give
3. Some-one to guide me I need-ed to know, Some-one the path-way to

life com-plete, Then I met Je-sus— I fell at His feet;
peace of mind, Then I met Je-sus— so gra-cious and kind;
Heav-en show, Then I met Je-sus— now on-ward I go

He was the Some-one who loved me. Some-one to love me, Real-ly, tru-ly
He was the One who could save me. Some-one to save me, From sin's pow-er
Walk-ing to Heav-en with Je-sus. Some-one to guide me, Safe-ly up-ward

© 1956 by Alfred B. Smith. Assigned to Singspiration, Inc. All rights reserved.

SOMEONE

love me; When I met Je-sus, I met the One who did love me.
save me; When I met Je-sus, I met the One who could save me.
guide me; When I met Je-sus, I met the One who could guide me.

JUST ABIDE 60

John R. Clements
COPYRIGHT, 1943, RENEWAL. THE RODEHEAVER CO., OWNER
INTERNATIONAL COPYRIGHT SECURED
B. D. Ackley

1. Is the day's load heav-y? Just a-bide; And the day's road
2. Is the day's heat blighting? Just a-bide; And the worn feet
3. Is your life song mi-nor? Just a-bide; Nights are long and

ston-y? Just a-bide; If your heart is grow-ing wea-ry, And your
wea-ry? Just a-bide; Pil-grim's songs in notes all-thrill-ing, And the
star-less? Just a-bide; Nev-er cloud but sil-ver lin-ing, For the

sky is gray and drear-y, Just a-bide, and keep on a-bid-ing.
soul with rap-ture fill-ing, Just a-bide, and keep on a-bid-ing.
sun is somewhere shin-ing, Just a-bide, and keep on a-bid-ing.

61 I FELL ON MY KNEES AND CRIED, "HOLY"

NETTIE DUDLEY WASHINGTON
E. M. DUDLEY CANTWELL

1. I dreamed of that cit-y called glo-ry, so bright and so fair. When I en-tered the gate I cried, "Ho-ly;" the an-gels all wel-comed me there. They led me from man-sion to man-sion, and, oh, the sights I saw. But I said, "I want to see Je-sus, the One who died for all."

2. I thought when I en-tered that cit-y, my loved ones knew me well. They showed me all through Hea-ven; the scenes are too num'rous to tell. I saw Ab-raham, I-saac and Ja-cob, Mark, Luke and Tim-o-thy. But I said, "Let me bow down and wor-ship the One who died for me."

3. I thought when I saw my dear Sav-iour, there seat-ed on His throne, Oh the won-der that He could love me, and call me His ve-ry own. I bowed down and wor-shipped this Sav-iour my friend of Cal-va-ry, And I want-ed to praise Him for-ev-er for sav-ing one like me.

Copyright 1923 by Nettie Dudley Washington. Copyright renewed and assigned to Hill & Range, Inc.

I FELL ON MY KNEES AND CRIED, "HOLY"

CHORUS

Then I fell on my knees and cried, "Ho-ly," ("Ho-ly,") "Ho-ly,"
("Ho-ly,") "Ho-ly," ("Ho-ly.") I fell at His feet and sang, "Glo-ry,
(Glo-ry,) glo-ry to the Son of God." Son of God." (of God.")

THE GREAT CREATOR

62

DAVID G. BALL

JOHN H. LANDGRAF, Jr.

1. How I praise the great Cre-a-tor, Who did make this world so fair;
2. In the steep and on the hill-top, There I find His roy-al throne,
3. Ti-ny bud and love-ly flow-er, All the fra-grant bloom of spring,
4. Bub-bling spring and swirl-ing riv-er, Lap-ping lake and toss-ing sea,
5. How I praise the great Cre-a-tor, Who did make this world so fair;

As I scan the realm of na-ture I can see His im-age there.
And the God who made the moun-tain Ev-er loves me as His own.
Show the sweet-ness and the beau-ty Of my Sov-'reign and my King.
All de-clare the might and great-ness Of the one who cares for me.
For I too am His cre-a-tion And I love Him for His care.

© 1955 by David Ball & John Landgraf. Assigned to Singspiration, Inc. All rights reserved.

BROKENHEARTED

COPYRIGHT, 1948, BY THE RODEHEAVER COMPANY
INTERNATIONAL COPYRIGHT SECURED

A. H. ACKLEY
B. D. ACKLEY

1. Time can nev-er heal the deep-est sor-row, There's no balm on earth for bro-ken hearts. Christ, the Lord a-lone can give you com-fort, Need-ed grace His love im-parts.
2. Then have faith in God, be-lieve His prom-ise, Lay hold of Christ, His bless-ed Son Trust the great Phy-si-cian that can help you, He's the One, the on-ly One.

REFRAIN

Bro-ken heart-ed, bro-ken heart-ed, On the cross His heart was bro-ken too; Bro-ken heart-ed, bro-ken heart-ed, He can heal your bro-ken heart, your bro-ken heart for you.

CALVARY CONQUERED MY HEART

64

J.W.P.
JOHN W. PETERSON

1. I was a reb-el and stran-ger from God, Wil-ful and self-ish the path that I trod; Care-less-ly walk-ing sin's high-way so broad When Cal-va-ry conquered my heart!
2. Just to be-hold Him—my Sav-iour so fair— Bleed-ing and dy-ing in a-go-ny there, Know-ing my sin in Him-self He did bear Made Cal-va-ry con-quer my heart.
3. Now He has won me—I'm His ev-er-more, Glad-ly I'll wor-ship Him— love and a-dore; Here on earth's jour-ney to Heav-en's bright shore For Cal-va-ry con-quered my heart!

CHORUS

Cal-va-ry conquered my heart!___ When I gazed on the tree, Saw Christ dy-ing for me Then Cal-va-ry con-quered my heart!___

© 1956 by Alfred B. Smith. Assigned to Singspiration, Inc. All rights reserved.

MY DESIRE

Words and Music by
THOMAS A. DORSEY

Andante ad lib.

Voice ad lib with spirit

It's My De - sire to do some good thing ev - 'ry day, It's My De - sire to help the fall - en by the way, It's My De - sire to bring back those who've

It's My De - sire to teach some sin - ner how to pray, It's My De - sire to help some trav - ler find the way, It's My De - sire to lift up Jes - us

Copyright 1937 by Thomas A. Dorsey
Copyright assigned 1951 to **HILL AND RANGE SONGS, INC.**, New York, N. Y.
Copyright 1951 by **HILL AND RANGE SONGS, INC.**, New York, N. Y.
International Copyright Secured   Printed in U.S.A.
All rights reserved including the right of public performance for profit.

MY DESIRE

gone a-stray, It's My De-sire to be like the Lord.
ev-'ry day, It's My De-sire to be like the Lord.

It's My De-sire to bring some wand-'rer to the fold, It's My De-
It's My De-sire to see His face when life is done, It's My De-

sire to shel-ter some one from the cold, It's My De-sire to do Thy will as
sire to meet the Fa-ther and the Son, It's My De-sire to hear Him say-"My

I am told, It's My De-sire to be like my Lord.
child well done," It's My De-sire to be like my Lord.

66 BURDENS ARE LIFTED AT CALVARY
(MIXED VOICES ARRANGEMENT)

JOHN M. MOORE.   JOHN M. MOORE.

1. Days are filled with sor-row and care, Hearts are lone-ly and drear;
2. Cast your care on Je-sus to-day, Leave your worry and fear,
3. Troubled soul, the Saviour can see Ev-'ry heartache and tear.

Burdens are lift - ed at Cal - va-ry, Je-sus is ve - ry near.
Burdens are lift - ed at Cal - va-ry, Je-sus is ve - ry near.
Burdens are lift - ed at Cal - va-ry, Je-sus is ve - ry near.

CHORUS.

Burdens are lift - ed at Cal - va-ry, Cal - va-ry, Cal - va-ry;

Burdens are lift - ed at Cal - va-ry, Je-sus is ve - ry near.

Copyright 1952 by John M. Moore. Assigned to Singspiration, Inc. All rights reserved.

# WHY?

J. M. Moore. — Medium Voice Arrangement. — **J. M. Moore.**

1. Why did they nail Him to Calvary's Tree? Why? tell me, why was He there? Jesus the Helper, the Healer, the Friend, Why? tell me, why was He there?
2. Why should He love me, a sinner undone? Why? tell me, why should He care? I do not merit the love He has shown, Why? tell me, why should He care?
3. Why should I linger afar from His love? Why? tell me, why should I fear? Somehow I know I should venture and prove, Why? tell me, why should I fear?

All my iniquities on Him were laid, He nail'd them all to the Tree; Jesus the debt of my sinfully paid, He paid the ransom for me.

Copyright 1953 by John M. Moore. Assigned to Singspiration, Inc. All rights reserved.

68. WHEN I KNEEL DOWN TO PRAY

A. H. Ackley
B. D. Ackley

COPYRIGHT 1948 BY THE RODEHEAVER CO.
INTERNATIONAL COPYRIGHT SECURED

1. Some-how the Sav-iour seems a lit-tle near-er, When I kneel down to pray, And fel-low-ship with Him a lit-tle dear-er,
2. A se-cret place of qui-et med-i-ta-tion, When I kneel down to pray, In-creas-es all the joy of that re-la-tion,
3. I tar-ry there with Christ a lit-tle long-er, When I kneel down to pray, And rise to face the world a lit-tle strong-er,

When I kneel down to pray.

REFRAIN

I know that He will al-ways hear me, For He is nev-er far a-way, And yet He seems a lit-tle clos-er to me, When I kneel down to pray.

OTHERS
69

Charles D. Meigs (Solo, Duet, or Trio) Alfred B. Smith

1. Lord help me live from day to day, In such a self-for-get-ful way,
2. Help me in all the work I do, To ev-er be sin-cere and true,
3. Let "self" be cru-ci-fied and slain, And bur-ied deep; and all in vain
4. And when on earth my work is done, And my new work in heav'n's be-gun,

That e-ven when I kneel to pray, My prayer shall be for OTH-ERS.
And know that all I'd do for you, Must needs be done for OTH-ERS.
May ef-forts be to rise a-gain, Un-less to live for OTH-ERS.
May I for-get the crown I've won, While thinking still of OTH-ERS.

CHORUS

Oth-ers, Lord, yes, oth-ers, Let this my mot-to be.
Help me to live for oth-ers, That I may live like Thee;
Help me to live for oth-ers, That I may live like Thee.

© 1956 by Singspiration, Inc. All rights reserved.

70 HEART TO HEART

H. D. L.   SOLO   Harry Dixon Loes

1. Heart to heart, I love to talk with Je - sus,
2. Doubts and fears— I bring them all to Je - sus,
3. I would pray, "Show me Thy will, O Fa - ther,

Bowed in the se - cret place; .... Shut the door,
He makes them dis - ap - pear; .... Calmed my soul,
Crush ev - 'ry vain de - sire; ..... Search me, Lord,

to all that would disturb me, I view His hal - lowed face. ....
I rise with faith and cour-age, To show a love sin - cere. ....
reveal my sins and weak-ness, A ho - lier life in - spire." ...

Refrain

'Tis there I learn to know Him, For He Him-self re - veals;

rit.

He understands my longing, My ev-'ry sorrow feels. Heart to heart,

Copyright 1948 by Harry Dixon Loes. Assigned to Singspiration, Inc. All rights reserved.

HEART TO HEART

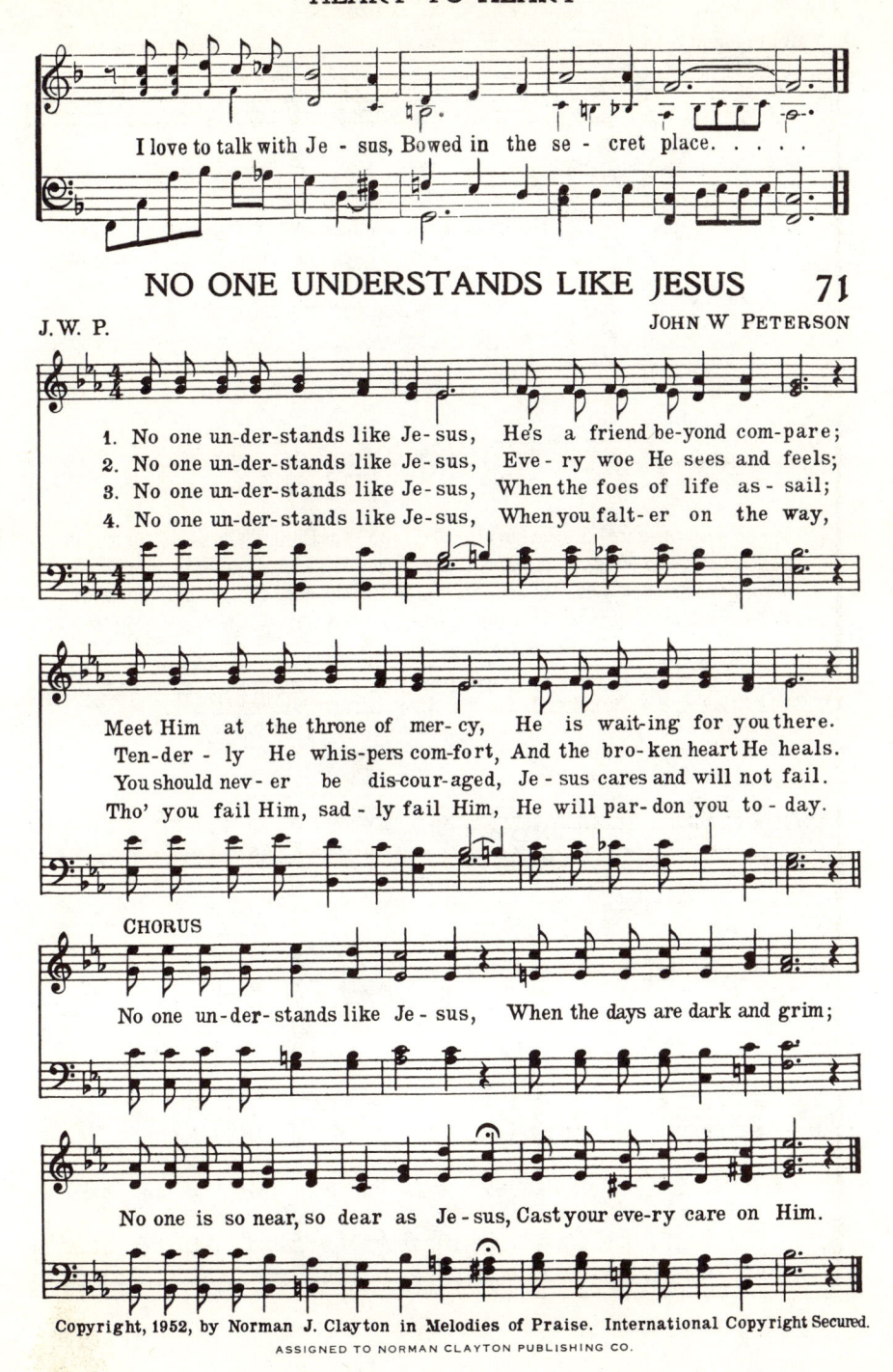

I love to talk with Je-sus, Bowed in the se-cret place. . . . .

NO ONE UNDERSTANDS LIKE JESUS 71

J. W. P.
JOHN W PETERSON

1. No one un-der-stands like Je-sus, He's a friend be-yond com-pare;
2. No one un-der-stands like Je-sus, Eve-ry woe He sees and feels;
3. No one un-der-stands like Je-sus, When the foes of life as-sail;
4. No one un-der-stands like Je-sus, When you falt-er on the way,

Meet Him at the throne of mer-cy, He is wait-ing for you there.
Ten-der-ly He whis-pers com-fort, And the bro-ken heart He heals.
You should nev-er be dis-cour-aged, Je-sus cares and will not fail.
Tho' you fail Him, sad-ly fail Him, He will par-don you to-day.

CHORUS

No one un-der-stands like Je-sus, When the days are dark and grim;
No one is so near, so dear as Je-sus, Cast your eve-ry care on Him.

Copyright, 1952, by Norman J. Clayton in Melodies of Praise. International Copyright Secured.
ASSIGNED TO NORMAN CLAYTON PUBLISHING CO.

72. FACE TO FACE

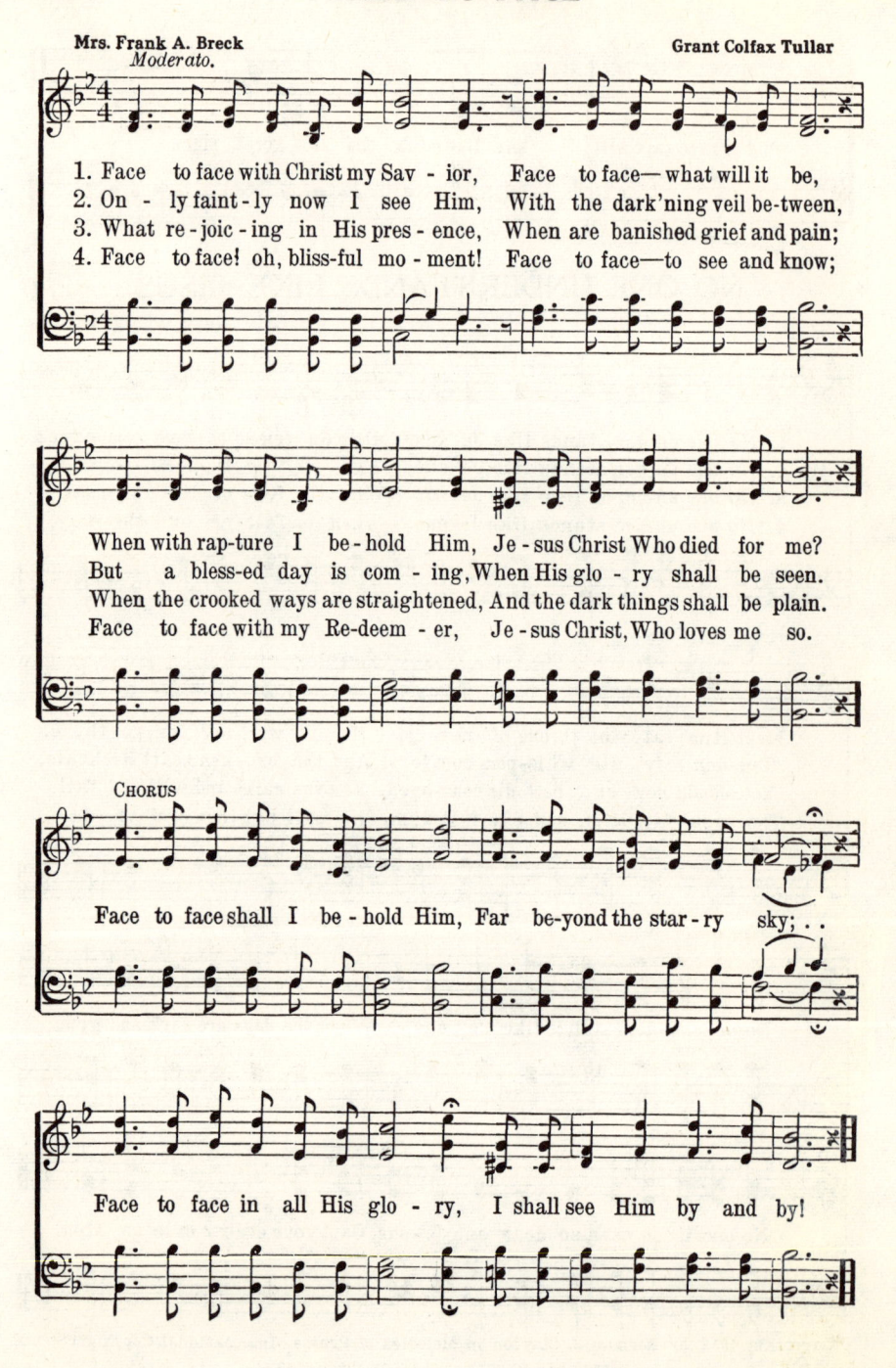

Mrs. Frank A. Breck
Moderato.
Grant Colfax Tullar

1. Face to face with Christ my Savior, Face to face—what will it be,
   When with rapture I behold Him, Jesus Christ Who died for me?
2. Only faintly now I see Him, With the dark'ning veil between,
   But a bless-ed day is coming, When His glory shall be seen.
3. What rejoicing in His presence, When are banished grief and pain;
   When the crooked ways are straightened, And the dark things shall be plain.
4. Face to face! oh, blissful moment! Face to face—to see and know;
   Face to face with my Redeemer, Jesus Christ, Who loves me so.

Chorus

Face to face shall I behold Him, Far beyond the starry sky;
Face to face in all His glory, I shall see Him by and by!

THE DAY WITHOUT A CLOUD

73

COPYRIGHT, 1928. RENEWAL, 1956
THE RODEHEAVER CO., OWNER
INTERNATIONAL COPYRIGHT SECURED

Rev. A. H. Ackley　　　　　　　　　　　　　　　　　　　　　B. D. Ackley

1. The clouds of grief o'ershadow The sky of time and sense, The path grows dark before us, And fills us with suspense, But tho' life's fair-est morning Be covered with a shroud, We'll see in heaven's dawning The day without a cloud.
2. The grief that o-ver-takes us Shall one day pass a-way, The troubles that dis-tress us Shall last but for a day; Our soul so worn and wea-ry, With perfect life endowed, Shall greet in God's great morning The day without a cloud.
3. The fac-es long for-got-ten Shall smile as oft be-fore, And voic-es long since si-lenced Shall greet us as of yore, And with the ransomed cho-rus We'll sing of Christ a-loud, Thanks be to God who gave us The day without a cloud.

Chorus.

The day......without a cloud, The day.....without a cloud;

rit.

Sometime, somewhere, we too, shall share God's perfect day, with-out a cloud.

pp

74 CAN I FORGET?

Harriet E. Jones
George S. Schuler

1. Can I for-get when from the throne The light di-vine en-
2. Oh, no, the love that filled my soul, I nev-er, nev-er
3. No word of mine can e'er ex-press The peace and joy then
4. Come, sin-ners, come the light to see That shines so bright from

cir-cled me, When Je-sus claimed me as His own, When
can for-get, For Je-sus held com-plete con-trol, O
giv'n to me, None can im-part such bless-ed-ness As
heav-en's throne, Come find the peace that waits for thee, That's

rit.

Chorus

I His bless-ed face did see!
sweet the time when first we met.   Can I for-get? Ah
Christ, the Lamb of Cal-va-ry.
found in Christ and Him a-lone.

no, ah no, I nev-er can for-get........... The
for-get,

time and place of long a-go, When Christ and I first met.

Copyright Renewal 1951 by George S. Schuler   ASSIGNED TO THE RODEHEAVER CO.

SOMEBODY CARES

75

© COPYRIGHT 1910. RENEWAL 1938 (EXTENDED) BY
THE RODEHEAVER CO., OWNER.

FANNIE EDNA STAFFORD

HOMER A. RODEHEAVER

1. Some-bod-y knows when your heart aches, And ev'rything seems to go wrong;
2. Some-bod-y cares when you're tempted, And your mind grows dizzy and dim;
3. Some-bod-y loves you when wea-ry; Somebody loves you when strong;

Some-bod-y knows when the shadows Need chasing a-way with a song;
Some-bod-y cares when you're weakest, And farthest a-way from Him;
Al-ways is wait-ing to help you, He watches you—one of the throng

Some-bod-y knows when you're lonely, Tir-ed, dis-cour-aged and blue;
Some-bod-y grieves when you're fallen, You are not lost from His sight;
Need-ing His friendship so ho-ly, Need-ing His watch-care so true;

Some-bod-y wants you to know Him, And know that He dear-ly loves you.
Some-bod-y waits for your com-ing, And He'll drive the gloom from your night.
His name? We call His name Je-sus; He loves ev-'ry-one, He loves you.

WHEN I'VE DONE MY BEST

Words and Music by
THOMAS A. DORSEY

Slow with Spirit

When I've done the best I can, If my friends don't un-der-stand,
When I've done the best I can, And I'm near the Prom-ised Land,

Then my Lord will car-ry me Home. Af-ter I have done my best,
Then my Lord will car-ry me Home. When my best I've tried to live,

I will find a peace-ful rest, When my Sav-ior car-ries me Home.
My mis-takes He will for-give, When my Sav-ior car-ries me Home.

Copyright 1939 by Thomas A. Dorsey
Copyright assigned 1951 to **HILL AND RANGE SONGS, INC.**, New York, N. Y.
Copyright 1951 by **HILL AND RANGE SONGS, INC.**, New York, N. Y.
International Copyright Secured   Printed in U.S.A.
All rights reserved including the right of public performance for profit.

WHEN I'VE DONE MY BEST

Man-y griefs and sor-rows I have wit-nessed on my part,
When my day is o-ver and the eve-ning shad-ows fall,

On that bright to-mor-row, He will mend and heal my wound-ed heart,
Faith will cross me o-ver, When I hear my Mas-ter sweet-ly call,

When the best I've done for Thee, Then the best comes back to me,
In my friends the best I see, May they see the best in me,

When my Sav-ior car-ries me Home.
When my Sav-ior car-ries me Home.

77 I HAVE BUILT A THRONE FOR JESUS

©COPYRIGHT 1935. RENEWED 1963 BY THE RODEHEAVER CO.
INTERNATIONAL COPYRIGHT SECURED.
ALL RIGHTS RESERVED.

Clarence Edwin Flynn Bertha Mae Lillenas

1. I have made my life a king-dom, and for-ev-er and a day, Tho' I
2. I have made Him Lord and Rul-er of this lit-tle world of mine, I have
3. I have peace and rest and blessing more than tongue could ever tell, And I

jour-ney in the des-ert or the mart; I have wrought a crown and scep-ter
cho-sen for my-self the bet-ter part; Of this won-der-ful do-min-ion
nev-er-more would think to dwell a-part; I have crowned Him King for-ev-er,

as the sym-bol of its sway, I have built a throne for Je-sus in my heart.
I have made the cross the sign, I have built a throne for Je-sus in my heart.
and I know that all is well, I have built a throne for Je-sus in my heart.

CHORUS

I have built a throne for Je-sus in my heart, . . . From that throne He never,
in my heart,

nev-er shall de-part; . . . . . He shall have complete con-trol of the
shall de-part;

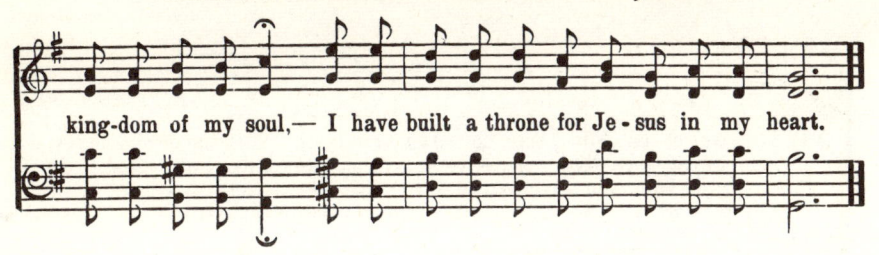

I HAVE BUILT A THRONE FOR JESUS

king-dom of my soul,— I have built a throne for Je-sus in my heart.

THERE SHALL BE NO TEARS

© COPYRIGHT 1938. RENEWED 1966 BY THE RODEHEAVER CO., OWNER.
INTERNATIONAL COPYRIGHT SECURED.
ALL RIGHTS RESERVED.

A. H. A.
A. H. Ackley

1. Be-yond the sun-set and the shade, The radiant morn of God ap-pears,
2. Be-yond the weariness God's rest A-bides for all who en-ter in;
3. Be-yond the years that soon shall end, Are changeless seasons of de-light,
4. Be-yond the sor-row of farewell, The broken heart, the failing breath,

Where none shall ev-er be a-fraid, And there shall be no tears,—no tears.
Where souls for-ev-er shall be blest, And there shall be no sin,— no sin!
The fleet-ing joys of time por-tend, And there shall be no night.—no night!
God's love shall ev'ry foe dis-pel, And there shall be no death,—no death!

79 SPRINGS OF LIVING WATER

J. W. P.
John W. Peterson

1. I thirsted in the barren land of sin and shame, And nothing satisfying there I found; But to the blessed cross of Christ one day I came, Where springs of living water did abound.
2. How sweet the living water from the hills of God, It makes me glad and happy all the way; Now glory, grace and blessing mark the path I've trod, I'm shouting "Hallelujah" ev-'ry day.
3. O sinner, won't you come today to Calvary, A fountain there is flowing deep and wide; The Saviour now invites you to the water free, Where thirsting spirits can be satisfied.

CHORUS

Drinking at the springs of living water, Happy now am I, My soul they satisfy; Happy now am I, My soul they satisfy; I'm Drinking at the

Copyright 1950 by Alfred B. Smith. Assigned to Singspiration, Inc. All rights reserved.

springs of living water, O wonderful and bountiful supply.

OH, WHAT A WONDERFUL DAY! 80

S. E. C.
Sidney E. Cox

1. The Saviour sought and found me, Far from the narrow way; He made my blinded eyes to see On that wonderful, wonderful day.
2. He lifted sin's great burden, He saw my deep dismay, And graciously He pardoned me On that wonderful, wonderful day.
3. My sin was red like crimson, He washed it all away; He filled my heart with melody On that wonderful, wonderful day.

CHORUS

He sought me, He sought me, When I was wandering far away; He found me, He found me: Oh, what a wonderful day!

© 1956 by Alfred B. Smith. Assigned to Singspiration, Inc. All rights reserved.

81. JESUS

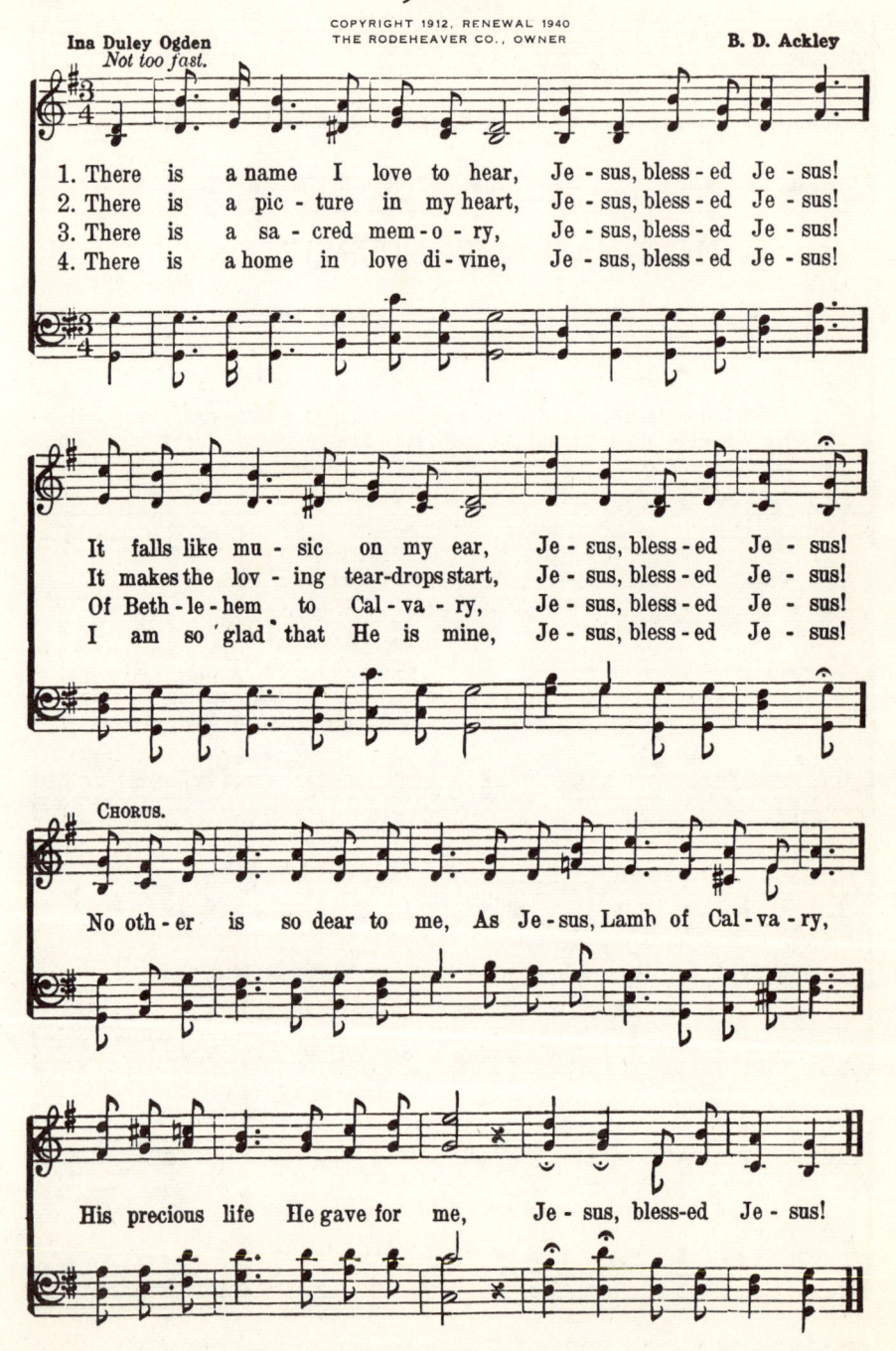

Ina Duley Ogden
Not too fast.
B. D. Ackley

COPYRIGHT 1912, RENEWAL 1940
THE RODEHEAVER CO., OWNER

1. There is a name I love to hear, Jesus, blessed Jesus!
2. There is a picture in my heart, Jesus, blessed Jesus!
3. There is a sacred memory, Jesus, blessed Jesus!
4. There is a home in love divine, Jesus, blessed Jesus!

It falls like music on my ear, Jesus, blessed Jesus!
It makes the loving tear-drops start, Jesus, blessed Jesus!
Of Bethlehem to Calvary, Jesus, blessed Jesus!
I am so glad that He is mine, Jesus, blessed Jesus!

CHORUS.

No other is so dear to me, As Jesus, Lamb of Calvary,
His precious life He gave for me, Jesus, blessed Jesus!

MY SOUL DELIGHTS

COPYRIGHT, 1930, RENEWAL, 1958
THE RODEHEAVER CO., OWNER
INTERNATIONAL COPYRIGHT SECURED

Gertrude R. Dugan
George S. Schuler

Introduction DUET

1. I have in heav'n a Friend so dear, Who sends me light and hope and cheer; He gave His precious life for me Upon the cross of Calvary.
2. O'er all my way His hand I see, Directing and upholding me; No day so full of grief, or care, No night so dark but He is there.
3. And if my burden heavy be, His arm supports my load and me, While over pathways all untrod He leads me on and up to God.

REFRAIN

O hallelujah! Praise His name! My soul delights in Christ my Lord;
O hallelujah! Praise His name! My soul delights in Christ my Lord.

83 NAILED TO THE CROSS

Mrs. Frank A. Breck
Grant Colfax Tullar

1. There was One who was will-ing to die in my stead, That a soul so un-wor-thy might live; And the path to the cross He was will-ing to tread, All the sins of my life to for-give.
2. He is ten-der and lov-ing and pa-tient with me, While He cleans-es my heart of the dross; But "there's no con-dem-na-tion"—I know I am free, For my sins are all nailed to the cross.
3. I will cling to my Sav-ior and nev-er de-part—I will joy-ful-ly jour-ney each day. With a song on my lips and a song in my heart, That my sins have been tak-en a-way.

REFRAIN

They are nailed to the cross, They are nailed to the cross, O how much He was will-ing to bear! With what an-guish and loss Je-sus went to the cross! But He carried my sins with Him there.

I WANT TO DO MY BEST

Virgil P. Brock … Blanche Kerr Brock

1. I want to do my best for Jesus, Because He did so much for me; No other one could be so worthy Of all my love and loyalty.
2. Tho' vile was I He died to save me, He covered all my guilt and sin; And though unworthy yet He loved me, So I must do my best for Him.
3. My life, my all I give to Jesus, My talents at His feet I lay; My hands, my feet shall do His bidding, My lips shall speak for Him alway.
4. If I withhold complete devotion, Some day 'twill be my deepest shame; Less than my best cannot but grieve Him, Who gave His all my all to claim.

Chorus

I want to do my best for Jesus, Because He did so much for me; No other one could be so worthy Of all my love and loyalty.

85 THERE'LL BE ONE SONG

MARGARET W. BROWN
HOWARD L. BROWN

1. There was one song in the be-gin-ning 'Ere earth was formed or time be-gun, When morn-ing stars all sang to-geth-er In ad-o-ra-tion of the Ho-ly One.
2. When Christ was born in low-ly man-ger The an-gel host with shin-ing wings Sang songs of praise and ad-u-la-tion A-bove the cra-dle of the King of Kings.
3. When time has ceased and earth has van-ished, The ran-somed souls of ev-'ry race Will sing one song in Heav-en's glo-ry Where they shall see the Sav-iour face to face.

CHORUS *Slowly*

There'll be one song thro' count-less a-ges, There'll be one song, one song a-lone, That song will be of Christ the Sav-iour, The Great Re-deem-er up-on His throne.

Copyright 1945 by Howard L. Brown. Assigned to Singspiration, Inc. All rights reserved.

IF YOU KNOW THE LORD

86

B.R.

BICKLEY REICHNER

With feeling – not fast

If you know the Lord, ____ You need no-bo-dy else ____ To see you through ____ the dark-est night. ____ You can walk a-lone, ____ You on-ly need the Lord, ____ He'll keep you on ____ the road marked right. ____ Take time to pray ____ ev-'ry day, ____ And when you're head-in' home ____ He'll show you the way. ____ If you know the Lord, ____ You need no-bo-dy else, ____ to see the light, ____ His won-der-ful light.

Copyright 1951 by Malvern Music Co.   Used by permission

'Sheet music of this fine song available at Malvern Music Co., Malvern, Pennsylvania.

87 I SING OF THEE

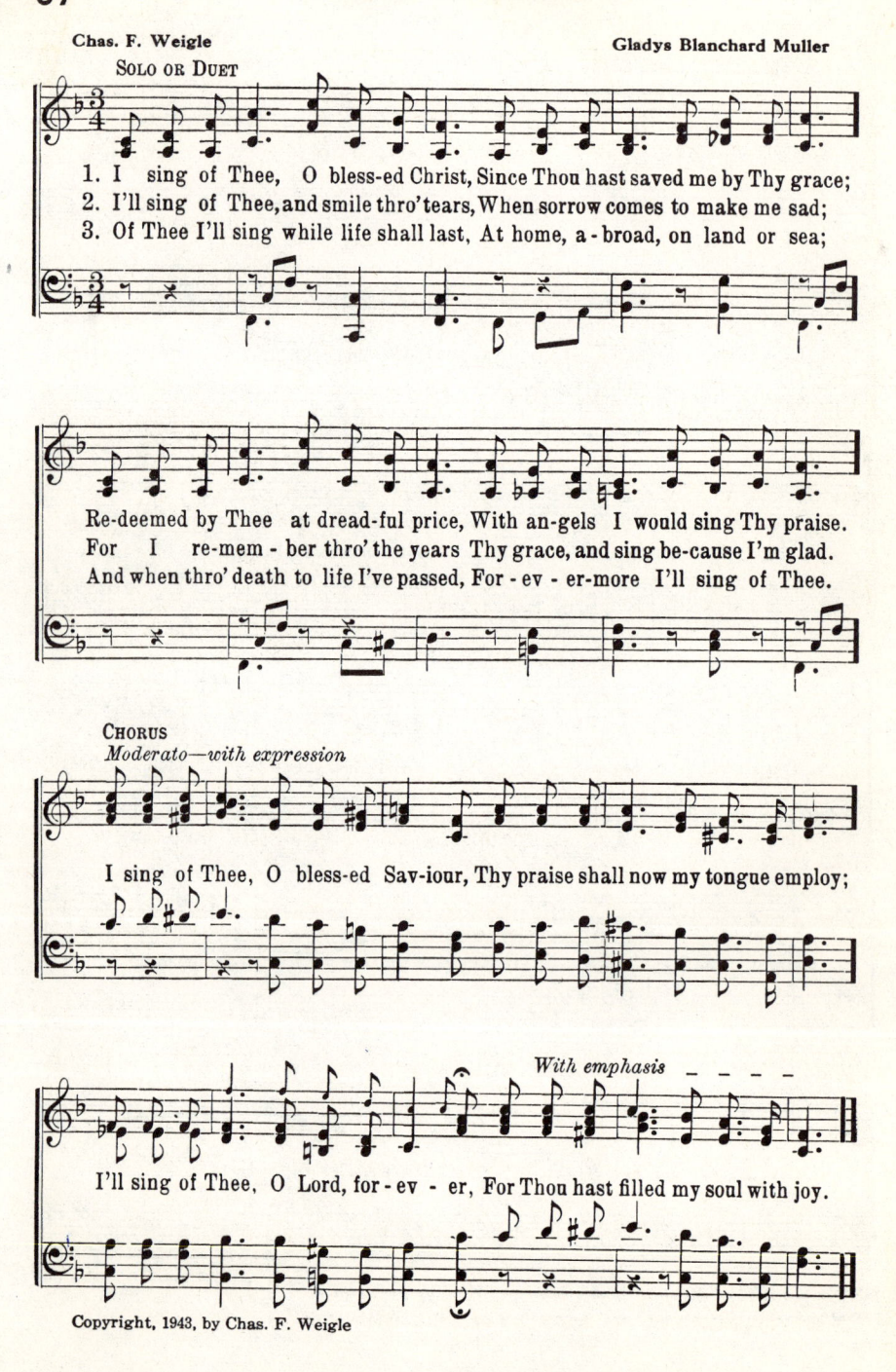

Chas. F. Weigle — Gladys Blanchard Muller

SOLO OR DUET

1. I sing of Thee, O bless-ed Christ, Since Thou hast saved me by Thy grace;
2. I'll sing of Thee, and smile thro' tears, When sorrow comes to make me sad;
3. Of Thee I'll sing while life shall last, At home, a-broad, on land or sea;

Re-deemed by Thee at dread-ful price, With an-gels I would sing Thy praise.
For I re-mem-ber thro' the years Thy grace, and sing be-cause I'm glad.
And when thro' death to life I've passed, For-ev-er-more I'll sing of Thee.

CHORUS
Moderato—with expression

I sing of Thee, O bless-ed Sav-iour, Thy praise shall now my tongue employ;

With emphasis

I'll sing of Thee, O Lord, for-ev-er, For Thou hast filled my soul with joy.

Copyright, 1943, by Chas. F. Weigle

OVER THE SUNSET MOUNTAINS

J. W. P.
John W. Peterson

1. O-ver the sun-set moun-tains, Some-day I'll soft-ly go;
2. Toiling will all be end-ed, Shad-ows will flee a-way;

In-to the arms of Je-sus, He who has loved me so.
Sor-row will be for-got-ten— Oh, what a won-der-ful day!

Chorus

O-ver the sun-set moun-tains Heav-en a-waits for me,

O-ver the sun-set moun-tains, Je-sus my Sav-iour I'll see.

Copyright 1953 by John W. Peterson. Assigned to Singspiration, Inc. All rights reserved.

89 O MIGHTY GOD, WHEN I BEHOLD THE WONDER

Carl Boberg, 1886
Free translation from Swedish by John Peterson
Swedish folk melody
Arr. by John Willard

Solo or duet

1. O mighty God, when I behold the wonder Of all the world so gloriously arrayed. The sun and moon and every star up yonder, And all the things Thy mighty hand hath made.
2. O loving God, when I behold a forest, And know that Thou hast planted every tree; In mem'ry's eye I see a tree on Cal-v'ry Where Thy dear Son was crucified for me.
3. When mists of time have like a vapor vanished, And all the saints are gathered 'round the throne; We'll sing Thy praise while ages roll unending, And worship Him who did for sin atone

CHORUS

My soul is filled with singing, Lord, to Thee, O mighty God, Great is Thy love.
My soul is filled with singing, Lord, to Thee, O mighty God, Great is Thy love.

© 1956 by Miracle Songs. Assigned to Singspiration, Inc. All rights reserved.